UNIVERSITY LIBRARY
W. S. U. - STEVENS POINT

P9-AOS-378

HEARING-IMPAIRED
PRESCHOOL CHILD

HEARING-IMPAIRED PRESCHOOL CHILD

A Book for Parents

By

JEAN E. SEMPLE, M.A.

Associate Professor
Department of Communication Disorders
St. Louis University
St. Louis, Missouri

With a Foreword by

Barbara J. Seelye, Ph.D.

Associate Professor and Chairman
Department of Communication Disorders
St. Louis University
St. Louis, Missouri

CHARLES C THOMAS • PUBLISHER
Springfield • Illinois • U.S.A.

Published and Distributed Throughout the World by

CHARLES C THOMAS • PUBLISHER

Bannerstone House

301-327 East Lawrence Avenue, Springfield, Illinois, U.S.A.

Natchez Plantation House

735 North Atlantic Boulevard, Fort Lauderdale, Florida, U.S.A.

This book is protected by copyright. No part of it
may be reproduced in any manner without written
permission from the publisher.

© 1970, *by* CHARLES C THOMAS • PUBLISHER

Library of Congress Catalog Card Number: 70-103587

*With THOMAS BOOKS careful attention is given to all details of
manufacturing and design. It is the Publisher's desire to present books that are
satisfactory as to their physical qualities and artistic possibilities and
appropriate for their particular use. THOMAS BOOKS will be true to those
laws of quality that assure a good name and good will.*

Printed in the United States of America

RN-10

HV
2395
.S4

FOREWORD

Dᴇᴀʀ ᴘᴀʀᴇɴᴛs:

What wonderful dreams you begin to envision when first you learn that a child is to be born. It does not seem to matter whether the child-to-be is the first to bless the home or the fifth to add laughter and the gentle innocence of the very young.

You can picture his happiness at the sounds and sights of the circus; his curiosity as he becomes aware of the songs of birds; the cries of other children at play; the soft purr of a sleepy kitten. You can see him as he runs to you at your call — the liveliest, healthiest child of them all.

And then, sometime after his birth, comes the realization that yours is a hearing-handicapped child. The knowledge may come with impact through the words spoken by your physician. Or it may seep slowly into your awareness as you observe deviant behavior patterns. It may come through the comments of a relative, friend or teacher. But, however the knowledge crystalizes, the seemingly unchangeable fact is there. Your child cannot hear within the normal spectrum of human ability to perceive sound. Your early dreams of his complete childhood dissolve in the frustration, anxiety and heartbreak normal to parents when learning that their child has a handicap. A myriad of questions arise and you begin to seek the answers.

In the case of the deaf or hard-of-hearing child, the first step is consultation with a physician specialized in problems of the ear, nose and throat. In some cases the hearing loss can be remediated through medical intervention. The otolaryngologist will be aware of any medical assistance with the problem. He may refer you to an audiologist for hearing testing so that the amount and type of loss may be ascertained. Such testing is available for infants and very young children as well as older children and adults.

196924

Recommendations for help can then be made by the otolaryngologist and the audiologist.

Assistance may take the form of a hearing aid and training in the use of the aid; and/or aural rehabilitation such as early training in the use of the remaining hearing, speechreading, or one of the other paths toward help known to the otolaryngologist, audiologist, aural rehabilitative specialist and teachers-of-the-deaf.

There still remains, to you, the question, What can I do? This is the purpose of this book. Drawing from her years of experience with deaf and hard-of-hearing children, and her sensitivity to and knowledge of the problems that perplex parents, Miss Semple has designed a book which touches upon the various aspects of child rearing made difficult by hearing loss. She discusses general child training, care of hearing aids, language and speech development, and, to her, the "meat" of the book, a series of lesson plans adaptable to any home situation.

Since problems in hearing are accompanied by problems in language and speech development, Chapter III may be of particular interest to parents as a foundation for the lessons in sound stimulation, discrimination and imitation which follow. Mr. Caccamo, a speech pathologist, has a deep interest in helping parents of handicapped children and their child in the communication process so necessary to adjustment in the environment today. Both he and Miss Semple are aware of the need for early teaching of the hearing impaired and the necessary role of parents in the teaching.

This book is not meant as a replacement for professional care and guidance but, rather, as an adjunct to such professional aid. It is an attempt to answer some common questions among parents and to lay a foundation for enlightened encouragement. It is written from an understanding and involvement with parents and deaf or hard-of-hearing children as they cooperatively weave together the experiences from which early dreams can be made a reality.

Barbara J. Seelye

PREFACE

So many times have you, the parents of the young hearing-handicapped child, asked, Where can I find something to read that will help me? There are many sources for material to which you could be sent, but no one book is available to cover the many aspects of the problems that you face. Often you do not live where you are in easy access to this knowledge you seek. This book has been written in an attempt to bring together much of this material for you. It is intended for any and all parents of the young preschool hearing-handicapped child. With this in mind, it is the sincere wish of the author that the material herewith contained will achieve this goal.

J.E.S.

INTRODUCTION

THERE first comes the suspicion that not all is well with the way your child responds to sounds and to speech around him. He does not turn when you call him; he does not come when you call him. He sleeps through the loud household noises; you run the vacuum cleaner through the room where he is sleeping. He does not awaken. The suspicions begin to crystallize; now you begin the search to find out if these suspicions are true. There is still the hope that you are wrong. But, finally, the otologist, the Hearing Clinic, or whoever does the assessment of the child's hearing, convinces you that your suspicions of a hearing loss are all too true. The shock of the realization is there now. "I don't want this to be true. My child cannot be deaf!" Now comes the greatest challenge. Can you accept the diagnosis without having feelings of guilt, without rationalizations for the cause, without blaming someone else for what has happened? After the shock of knowing the truth wears off, can you accept the problem as the experts in their field have told you? If you can, then you will start planning for your child's future.

You must think of what you can learn to do for him, not what has caused the condition. It is the future and the present that are now important, not what has already passed. Your attitude toward your child, toward what you can do yourself, and toward the other members of your family will determine how successful you can be in helping your child. You must think of what you can do to help your child to achieve to his maximum abilities, limited though they may appear in the first stages of his life. If you can learn to be happily accepting of your role as his helper, your child is well on his way to becoming a more independent and mature child. He will have a better chance to grow to live a life adjusted to his hearing handicap.

It is important to realize and to accept your child's potentialities, limited though they may seem to be, in order to plan realistically for his future. He must be encouraged and helped to use to the fullest extent his abilities which are those of any child. But he must not be pushed to achieve beyond the abilities he has. You must learn to know what your child can do and to work with him within this framework.

If feelings of guilt are there, you cannot give wholly in your efforts to help your child. He will always be the symbol of these feelings, if you allow them to remain. He will not be unaware of your feelings for him. This will hinder his progress, as well as yours in trying to help him to reach his level of achievement.

The word "deaf" has been used and is often used by you; you are likely to think of any hearing impairment of your child as that of deafness. The word "deaf" has slightly different meaning to many people. To some, any hearing loss is spoken of as deafness. Others use the word only for those whose hearing impairment is severe or profound. The word "deaf" will be used herein as meaning a severe hearing loss in which the child cannot receive language through the channel of hearing and thus must learn through other channels, such as vision. This book will be geared more for those who, with or without a hearing aid, may learn to hear and to speak the language of communication. This is the child who can function with audition. However, with the more severe hearing loss the lessons contained in the book could be adapted for speechreading lessons. If they are used for speechreading, the vision will be used more than the hearing.

In order to give you some guidance, this book will contain suggestions for the causes and for the handling of many behavioral problems arising from your child's inability to communicate with you and your inability to understand and communicate with him. Usually, your child will need a hearing aid which makes sounds and speech louder for him. What the hearing aid does, the care of it, and the operational problems arising from its use are discussed to assist you in coping with this extra problem. The purchase of the hearing aid will be under the direction of your otologist or audiologist in the Hearing Clinic.

An explanation of the language and speech problems has been

included to help you understand the stages of normal development and when there is a language problem. The hearing-impaired child's language and speech development will deviate from the normal scale. The hearing-impaired child will usually only deviate from the normal because he is not hearing the language in the same way as those who can hear normally. He may not be hearing enough of what is being said to cause him to show any interest in what those around him are saying. Or speech may not be loud enough for him to attach any meaning to what he hears; or he may be hearing nothing at all. For your child to learn to understand what you are saying to him, and for him to learn to speak, you must help him at home. This assistance is needed throughout his years of growing up. For this reason the lessons for home use have been included in this book.

The lesson outlines are intended to be adaptable for your particular home situation and as a guide for you. The lessons can be expanded or shortened for whatever is the need of your child and you. Materials are suggested, but you may have better ideas to use. It is hoped that you will not hesitate to put into use your own ideas, if they are going to assist your child to learn to understand what is being said and will help him to speak.

ACKNOWLEDGMENTS

I WOULD like to acknowledge the contributions that my colleague, James Caccamo, has made to this book through his chapter on "Language and Speech Development," and for his help in compilation of the sources of materials that is included in the appendices. I say thank you to him and to Dr. Barbara J. Seelye, Chairman of the Department of Communication Disorders, for her continuing interest in the book. My thanks, also, to Carolyn Wheeler for all the hours she spent typing the preliminary draft of the book.

J.E.S.

CONTENTS

HEARING-IMPAIRED
PRESCHOOL CHILD

Chapter I

THE PROBLEMS

Y OU, the parents of the hearing-impaired preschool children, have often many more behavioral problems with your child. His behavior may be such that you do not understand your child and you feel that you are not, or cannot, cope adequately with his acts. One of the questions most often asked by you is "How can I discipline my child? He is not like my other children." This is, indeed, a real problem in many homes. Your attitude toward your child may be, in many instances, a contributing factor or factors.

ATTITUDES

Let us first look at how you perceive your hearing-handicapped child as an individual. Your child's behavior and his ability to understand you when you are talking to him, or communicating in some way, may be different from your other children's behavior because he has hearing loss. This will be in degrees, of course, depending upon the amount of his hearing loss. The more severe the hearing loss is, the greater may be your problems; this is especially true when you are trying to make him understand what you are saying to him. In his physical and mental capacities he is, in all likelihood, as normal as your other children.

The first thing you must try to understand is your own feelings for your handicapped child. The second thing you must try to understand is your child's problem in communicating to you and your problem in communicating to him. You must understand these problems before you can effectively help your child, and, for that matter, help yourself.

All parents hope that their child will be "perfect" in all respects. That is, of course, only natural. But then "perfect" is only a matter of degree. A physical defect may seem to carry the greatest blow. With a hearing loss, however, there is no visible evidence of the handicap. People are less sympathetic and understanding of the person with a hearing deficiency because they cannot see the handicap. When the hearing aid is worn and seen by others, people do often respond by speaking louder to the person.

When you are told that your child does not hear normally, the traumatic experience of receiving such a diagnosis could well be almost a physical blow. Mrs. P was a young mother who had learned that her first child was not hearing normally. She had hoped, it is supposed, that such a thing could not really happen. When she had to accept the fact that he did have a hearing loss, she broke down and wept. Because the people who were making the investigation of the hearing and assessment of it were sympathetic and understanding of what she was experiencing, she soon rallied, after that first shock. She learned how she could help her child in the daily routines of her home and did much to help him adjust to his handicap and to learn to communicate with others.

✳ Feelings of guilt may appear, consciously or unconsciously. What have I done to have this happen to me and my child? Past indiscretions may intensify these feelings of guilt. For instance, you may have feelings of guilt for having exposed yourself during your pregnancy to the German measles which you knew were in the neighborhood at the time. Mrs. X became very angry with a neighbor of hers whose children had had a mild case of the German measles during the time that Mrs. X was pregnant. The children had been in her home. The neighbor had not told her that there was measles in her home. Mrs. X did not show symptoms of the disease herself; however, her son was born with a loss of hearing (fortunately, it was only a mild to moderate loss of hearing). When the hearing investigation and assessment was made by the clinical team, it was learned that the mother did have a very mild rash, during the time of the German measles epidemic; and the child's loss of hearing was laid to the maternal rubella. However, time and emotional state spent on self-recriminations, or in venting anger on others, is not going to help either your child or you. You must have a positive outlook on what can be done now and in the future. In all probability there was no control that you could have exercised that would have made the problem any different. Even though things might have been changed, or controlled, it is too late now to do anything. The past must not, and cannot, be relived. It is the present and the future with which you must cope.

You may deny the existence of a hearing loss in your child. This may happen even when the facts are undeniable. If you do deny the hearing loss in your child, and try to fool yourself and others into believing there is no hearing handicap, you are wasting valuable time which you could be using more profitably now. You could be doing positive things for helping to lessen your child's communicative handicap. Time is of the essence in the first three years of a child's life.

Often if the guilt complex is present, you will try to compensate for this by overprotecting your child. You will not let him do this or that because he cannot hear. You do everything for him, even to the extent of feeding him when he should be learning to do these things for himself. You smother him with maternal love and deny him his right to grow to independence and to the eventual social and emotional maturity that he can achieve. Mr. and Mrs. Y were overly protective and overly permissive with their infant daughter. They did all things for her; they allowed her to do as she pleased. At three years of age she was a pretty doll, tending toward obesity, undisciplined, without speech and language. Three years of time vital for helping the child had passed untouched. Those who saw her for the first time at the Speech and Hearing Clinic had all these factors to overcome as they assisted her and her parents to the art of communication and self-discipline. The child had ceased to grow mentally and emotionally. Some other child might have withdrawn from the flood of parental love and protection and mental and emotional growth would have been stunted. Perhaps another child would have rebelled, become aggressive with the other children and you would wonder what to do with him. He is frustrated with his inability to communicate with you and with others, and with your inability to understand his communications. Therefore, he overacts in one way or the other.

On the other hand you may, consciously or unconsciously, reject this child who is less perfect to you than your other children. You may, in these circumstances, do little for him aside from meeting his physical comforts. Again you deny him the right to grow mentally and emotionally. You do not deny your other children this right to grow to maturity. Mrs. G rejected her child, who was to her a symbol of what she wanted to forget. An infant is much aware of the feelings of the mother. Against the rejection Mrs. G's child felt, she withdrew from her environment into her own world. The evidence was obvious at eight months. It took much longer to reach this child and give her help. When such a state should arise, professional help should be sought for you both.

Innumerable times you and your child are going to become frustrated because of your inability to understand what you are attempting to say to each other. He will have temper tantrums many times a day. You will become frustrated with your inability to get across to him whatever it is that you want him to understand. You will possibly find yourself in a complete rage, if you do not learn to exercise patience. Patience on your part must be the key word in the handling and disciplining of the child. He needs your love and affection; so do your other children. If he feels rejected, or if he feels that his siblings are getting more of your love and attention than he, he may try many attention-getting behaviors. For you to give him too much of your time and attention may give him the feeling that he is something special. To grow up with such an unhealthy attitude will make it much more difficult for him to adjust to his place in society. He could be a spoiled, selfish, immature and unhappy adult. The hearing-handicapped child needs to take his place in the family life in the same way as the other children must. He must have the feeling of security that he does have his place in his home life and with the other members of his family. Feeling secure in his daily life aids him to adjust to his handicap and to accept it as a part of his way of life.

The other members of the family must help your handicapped child to learn to understand and to speak, too. They can help him when he needs help but they must not do everything for him. If this happens, he will never learn self-reliance; neither will he gain confidence in his own abilities.

Possibly, one of the more difficult problems you will have to cope with will be your own reactions and embarrassment when you are out in public with your child. Maybe you are shopping, and your child indicates he wants some candy; he indicates by grunts, or an overly loud vocalization unpleasant to the ear. You feel the color creeping into your face, and you become horribly embarrassed when the people around begin to look queerly at you and your child. You must learn to cope with such experiences without your child being aware of your reactions. He will soon lose confidence in his efforts to speak, if he feels your lack of confidence in him. Miss Z was taking three small hearing-handicapped boys for a demonstration of their communicative abilities before a large convention of interested people. They passed by a coat checkroom in the hotel where the meetings were being held. One woman in the room, when she saw the children with hearing aids, said to the other, "Look at the poor children; they can't hear." For Miss Z, who saw these children as happy, boisterous boys, normal in their abilities to get into mischief, this conversation which she had overheard aroused her annoyance. The instance was minor; but such instances can happen to you. You must learn to hear such remarks and show no reaction to them. The hearing persons' reactions to a hearing-impaired child's attempts to speak are often the result of a lack of understanding or a lack of knowledge of what a handicap can mean to a child and his parents. To them his behavior is strange, and, therefore, the behavior is not normal. Neither anger nor embarrassment will help you or him. Can you say without emotion, "My child has a hearing loss. He is just learning to speak." Can you recover from your embarrassment and cope with the situation without your child seeing your reactions?

When the stranger, or for that matter, some relative, gives into him always because of pity for the child, what is your reaction and attitude to this? How are you going to handle the problem? Whatever your attitude may be, you must always do for your child what is going to help him the most to have the opportunity for normal development. Your attitude should be one of patience and consistency to the behavioral problem which will be created for you by these people who give into him at all times and hinder his mental and emotional growth toward normalcy.

You may be faced with the problem of the neighbors' children not being allowed to play with your child because he has a hearing handicap; he is different. How will you react to this? It may be that the neighbors do not understand your child's problems and the problems which these will impose upon you. To be angry and annoyed with the neighbors will not help matters. Could you make your own backyard a pleasant place for all children to play and welcome the other children to your home? Giving your neighbor and the other children a chance to understand the problems of the hearing-handicapped child may make them more sympathetic toward both of you.

Sometime you will be faced with coping with a temper tantrum in a public place. What will be your attitude toward your child when this happens? You know that the display of frustration is because he does not understand the situation nor what you expect of him. The people around you do not know this. Can you remain calm, patient and unflustered by his behavior? You calmly try to make him understand; he does get the idea; the smile breaks forth. The crisis has passed; and you have won another bout with your child's behavioral problems, and you have a feeling of having overcome another obstacle on the path to communication with your child.

COMMUNICATION

Having given your child the emotional and physical needs he must have for normal growth and having achieved an understanding of your child and his problems, then the greatest challenge you will face will be to assist him in achieving communicative efficiency. You should always talk with him as you would with your other children and when you want him to do something, or you want him to understand something. You must make certain that he is facing you when you are speaking to him; make certain that you are close enough to him so that he may hear what you are saying. Do not try to call him from another room, even if he is wearing a hearing aid, and expect him to respond to your call. Your annoyance or anger for a lack of response is unjustified. If you find less responses from him than is the usual pattern when you are speaking to him, check his hearing aid for it may not be operating as usual. You should see that he does look at you when you speak to him; your face should be facing the light so that he can see you clearly.

You should always keep to the forefront of your thinking that he is first a child with all the normal potentials of a child; his hearing handicap is a second consideration. It will take longer at first to get the meaning you wish to convey to him across to him. You should make time for him and give him those extra few minutes that might mean the difference between him understanding and not understanding you. Let him see what you are talking about. If you ask him to get his coat, and he does not understand, then take him by the hand and go to where his coat is hanging and take it down for him to put on. At the same time you tell him that it is his coat. After many repetitions of this act in each situation demanding such an action, he will associate what he hears you say, and/or sees you say, with the object; then you will only need to give him the simple command. Again remember to make sure that you are close enough to him for him to hear you, and speak to him standing in front of him so that he might have a clear view of your face. In all instances speak normally, but not too quickly. You will not get him to understand you if you speak rapidly; be careful, however, not to mouth the words, that is, to use exaggerated mouth movements.

Use the same words and sentences in the same situation until he has learned to understand you either auditorily or visually. Hopefully it will be auditorily. Talk to him about his clothing as you dress and undress him, about the food he eats, about the utensils he uses during the meals, etc. Always have his attention before you begin to talk to him. All members of the family should help him to acquire the language and speech of everyday experiences. Each member should practice good habits for having him watch and listen.

At bedtime, or before naptime, tell him a simple story of several short simple sentences from a picture in a storybook that is before him. Hold the book so that he can see what you are saying and at the same time see the picture you are speaking about. During the day, when he is ready for communication, brief periods given to him to assist him to understand the language used around him will not deprive your other children of your time and attention. If you have difficulty finding time, budget your time daily, as you would your money, and work within this framework. Spread the time for helping him over the day, if this is possible with the care of your home and the other members of your family. To give him a lesson each day for half an hour and then forget about his communicative needs for the rest of the day will leave large gaps in his learning experiences and the acquisition of language and speech will be slow. The child learns from facial expressions, gestures and emotional quality of the voice. All of these are channels of communication. Do not use gestures as a substitution for speech and language; use gestures only if they complement speech and language. You must keep in mind that gestures are much more easily learned than language and speech. If you use many gestures, he will learn to communicate through these and not learn to speak.

Include your hearing-handicapped child in all the family activities. He may not know at first what the activity is all about; he may not know what the others are doing or what is expected from him; he may seem very confused or bewildered. This is better than not including him at all. In time he will learn and associate the appropriate meanings with the activities, although it may be some time still before he can use the correct words with the activities. Repetition of the same activity, in the same way, in each situation, helps his association of the language used with the activity. For example, each Friday evening, after dinner, all the family pile into the car to go to the grocery store for the week's groceries. You say to your handicapped child, "We are going shopping for the oranges." If he does not know any such word for food, show him an orange before you take him out to the car, and, after several experiences with you shopping for groceries, during which time you do buy oranges, he will begin to understand. When he learns more words, change the word you use as a substitute for groceries, until he begins to learn the meaning of the word *groceries.* The word *shopping* will be used each time, as well as *car, coat* (if this is applicable for the season of the year).

As long as you make the attempts to lessen his communicative disability, he will be learning. You may not readily see the results of your effort for some time. To fail is only not to try.

DISCIPLINE

The problem of discipline looms large with frustrations and doubts as to whether you are doing the right thing or not. If you allow it, your patience will be stretched to the limit many times. Your thinking can do much to determine how you will approach the problem.

You must always keep in mind that your hearing-handicapped child *is* a child first with all the needs and frustrations of a normal hearing child. Added to these problems are the problems he has because of his hearing loss. The problems of the hearing loss only compound the usual problems of any growing child which he also has. However, it is the problems arising from the hearing loss that affect his ability to communicate efficiently. It is the problems from the hearing loss which cause both you and him the greatest frustrations. Although he has the needs of the normal hearing child, neither you nor he must ever forget that he has a handicap from a hearing impairment. Both of you must learn to live with this handicap. But you must also meet his needs as a child as you would any child. He must be taught the difference between what behavior is acceptable and what behavior is unacceptable in the home and the society in which he must live. To guide him to this end will take a much greater effort on your part. Communication is the usual channel for instilling the mores of society. Your child's communication abilities are limited in these early years; and so your problems of teaching him are greater than with your other children.

When disciplinary actions are necessary, you must approach the problem calmly and always in a consistent pattern. Do not discipline him one way one time and in some other way the next time for the same "crime." It is difficult enough for him to understand you when he is reprimanded in one way. If he is bombarded in many ways, he will not learn to understand what meaning you are trying to get across to him. Repetition must be the pattern you follow even with discipline. If you use the same type of communication as each behavioral problem arises, he will soon associate your displeasure with his behavior. But, if you use different disciplinary actions each time something happens that calls for discipline, then he will never make the associations of your acts with his misbehavior. The same disciplinary action may not be necessary with your other children for you can more easily make them understand why they are being punished because they can hear you. With your under-two-years-olds of normal hearing you could have a problem of communication as well. Because they had not acquired much language as yet they, too, might have difficulty understanding why they were being punished. A consistency in your methods of discipline for the normal infant would also be necessary, and desirable. When your hearing-impaired child has learned there are certain types of behaviors that are acceptable and there are certain types that are unacceptable, then he will develop a feeling of security in his environment. He knows in which boundaries, or limitations, he can function without inflicting punishment upon himself.

He will have many more temper tantrums and frustrations than the normal hearing child; he has a disability in communication. His tantrums and frustrations are going to communicate themselves to you, too, if you do not remain calm and unemotional. He may become overly aggressive with his brothers and sisters; or he may withdraw from all contact with members of the family. You will not want either of these two possibilities to arise, if you can prevent them. If he feels that he is being neglected and the other children's needs are receiving more attention than his wants, he may use aggressive behavior in order to have more attention paid to himself. Include him in all the family activities, when this is possible, and have him participate actively. Take time to communicate to him what is about to happen or what you, he and the others are going to do. Each member in the family can help him in this way. Do not leave him sitting on the sidelines because no one has time to tell him what he is to do. This isolation for him is a shattering experience. He is very likely to react in some way. You must remember that he will not understand at first what you are trying to tell him; but after a few times of being helped through the activity, he will begin to make the appropriate associations and an understanding of language will begin.

There will be times when disciplinary actions call for a punishment to be meted out. When this happens, he must know why he is being punished. Show him what he has done wrong and that this is not the type of behavior that you expect or want from him. Again, and always, use speech, even though he still may not understand all or, for that matter, any of what you say. Your expression and gestures can indicate your displeasure. Approach the situations for discipline in the same way each time, and he will soon learn to associate your displeasure with his act and avoid doing what is bringing your displeasure upon himself. The question arises, What type of punishment should I use? This question could be answered with another one, What type of punishment did you use with your other children when they were his age? He has all the needs of a hearing child; but he has difficulty understanding what you are saying to him. Be sure that he is watching you and "listening" to you when you are indicating the errors of his ways.

The key to good disciplinary practices is calmness in your approach. His needs are those of any child; your problem is in communication and getting him to understand why this punishment is being inflicted upon him. For example, when you are faced with such "crimes" as swiping candy from the candy jar when you were not looking, and when he runs away or suddenly darts across the street in front of a car, and is just missed being knocked down, what will be the punishment for each? The first "crime" is a small wrong and something all children are likely to do at some time or other in their young lives — candy is a temptation. The second "crime" is an act which endangers his life and upsets you greatly. Two different types of disciplinary action is called for. In each instance he must learn the behavior is unacceptable; but, the behavior, which was dangerous to his welfare, must never happen again. The punishment should be that which will not be forgotten easily. Both these two types of behavior could be displayed with your hearing under-three-year-old. Your reactions and punishment would likely be the same. You must remember that your hearing-impaired child does need discipline just as his siblings do. If you love your child, you must help him to learn the language and speech of right and wrong, and eventually to learn self-discipline.

It was suggested that you would use the same form of discipline for him as you would for your other children. This may be modified at first for your handicapped child. It would be more on the basis of the pre-eighteen-month-old level. To send him to his room, or to put him to bed, for what he has done wrong, without having made him understand why these punishments were meted out, would have them fail in their intended use. These methods could only be used when he understands he is being punished for his misbehavior. A smart tap on his hands, or a smart slap on the seat of his pants, could be a form of punishment which he could feel and the same time he could see your facial expressions of displeasure. For example, if he upset his dish of cereal on the floor, you might say, "No, no, no! You must not do that!" At the same time you scowl and at the same time give the hand that did the act a smart tap, he would soon make the association between your scowl, tap, and the upsetting of the food on the floor. If the punishment is used repetitiously for the "crime," he would soon understand that "No, no, no!" along with your displeasure meant he should not upset his cereal. As you must always do, make sure when you are speaking to your child that you have his attention and see that you are close enough to him so that he can hear you as well as see you.

The type of discipline used on the very young hearing-handicapped child might have to be carried to an older age than with the normally hearing child. Once he begins to acquire language and can understand you some, then use whatever type of disciplinary measures that you would use with your other children. Just make sure that he understands for what he is being punished. Associate the punishment with whatever his unacceptable behavior was. Let the punishment fit the "crime." Be calm, patient, unemotional, and consistent in your approach to problems created by your child's behavior.

TOILET TRAINING

The principles of toilet training that you used with your other children would apply for your hearing-handicapped child too. Toilet training should be a happy and positive experience for the child. No anxiety should be aroused in the child. No discipline should be used to achieve the final goal. The child should understand what you are trying to achieve; he should not be confused by the attempts at training. You should keep in mind that he can punish you too by deliberately soiling his clothing when he is made unhappy.

You should not attempt toilet training too early. Begin when he is ready. Normally this is when he is twenty-four to twenty-eight-months-old, when his bladder is able to retain for a length of time, two hours or more. You should keep track of the periods when he is dry. Training pants would be helpful. When he is placed on the toilet seat sit down beside him and wait; do not leave him alone. It would be wise to begin toilet training in the season of the year when he would not be burdened down with so much clothing, especially outdoor clothing, as he would be in the wintertime. Dress him in clothing which he can easily manage himself. Always use the same word in referring to this training; for example, do you want to go to the bathroom? do you want to go to the toilet? let us go to the bathroom, or whatever. It is wise to use the words which he will use when he is older. It is difficult enough to teach him one concept without having to reteach him at a later date. Use the language to explain each step of the training procedure to him; use these same words each time you take him to the toilet. There will be accidents and many of them. Praise him when he remains dry. Once he has become accustomed to feeling dry, he will like this and be more likely to "tell" you when he needs to go to the toilet.

Toilet training will carry over into the night as well, once he remains dry during the day. By this time you will know how long a period he can go in between trips to the bathroom. Take him to the toilet before you retire for the night. You may feel that he should be taken during the evening hours as well. He can be aroused just enough to get him to the bathroom without arousing him completely. You might find that you will have to set the alarm to arouse yourself to take him to the bathroom during the early morning hours. You will have to determine the time element for a trip to the bathroom and help him within this framework. If you find your times do not coincide with his wet periods, then change the times you take him to the toilet until he goes through the nights without bed-wetting. A good rule to follow is to avoid giving him liquids before you put him to bed, or if he calls for a drink after he has been put to bed.

Your biggest trial may be in trying to remain unemotional during the attempts at training. Still, you must train your hearing-handicapped child as you would your other children; and keep at the toilet training until you succeed. Since the degree of communication between you and your child may be very limited or there may be no understanding at all, your greatest problem will be to get him to understand what you want him to do during this training; that is to have him understand he is to tell you when he is ready to go to the toilet. Approach the training positively. He may be able to get clues only from your facial expressions, actions and gestures. If this is necessary, you can use gestures with the appropriate words. Never try to communicate to him by other channels of communication without using speech with them. Be pleased when he responds positively, frown when he has not indicated to you that he wanted to "go" and has wet his clothing. In other words, by expressions show your pleasure and displeasure but never punish him. It might be possible to give him a small reward, such as an affectionate hug and kiss, when he has remained dry and conveyed to you his toilet needs. He must always know why he has been praised or rewarded. When accidents occur no signs of pleasure are forthcoming from you. You must have patience and plenty of it. Be always consistent in the method you use to toilet train, until you find it does not work satisfactorily; only then will you attempt to change your procedures.

If your child should have an upsetting emotional experience then he is likely to regress. Sammy was a preschool hearing-impaired child. He had been toilet trained and was not bed-wetting. When his infant sister arrived he was moved out of his room into his next older brother's bed. His brother was still bed-wetting, so Sammy joined him, and regressed. Sometimes these experiences may not be avoided. If he does regress, then training will have to begin again. You must not become discouraged. He must be trained before he is ready to start school.

You must think of him as a child with any child's needs and the need to learn just as your other children have needed to be taught. However for your hearing-impaired child, it may take longer and take more effort on your part to achieve the training. This is not because he has a hearing loss, but because of the poor communication between you and him. As he learns to understand through language, there will be a lessening of these communication difficulties. With effort on your part you will help him to achieve success in all the ways he must grow.

SUMMARY

This has been a discussion of the attitudes you may have toward your child's problems that will interfere with your understanding and your assistance which you might give your child who has a hearing impairment. Sound and positive attitudes on your part are necessary for mental and emotional growth of both you and your child. Discipline and toilet training are both areas which will result in frustrations if you cannot communicate effectively with him. Understanding of the problem, patience, and calmness are necessary ingredients for success.

Chapter II

HEARING AIDS

THE HEARING AID AND WHAT IT DOES

HEARING aids are mechanical devices which are for the sole purpose of amplifying, or making sounds louder, for the wearer. The young child cannot be expected to have language and speech as soon as he puts on the hearing aid. He must have instruction to learn the meaning of the sounds he does receive louder. This is true of sounds per se and of speech sounds. Language and speech just do not happen as soon as he wears the aid. You play a vital role in helping him to acquire these goals in the acquisition of language and speech.

The experience of the wearing of the hearing aid should always be a pleasant experience for the child. In the early period of wearing the aid, do not expose him to loud sounds or to loud noises. He could be frightened by these. You would then have the problem of trying to get him to wear the aid again. You must always speak in a normal tone of voice. You must not get into a habit of speaking loudly to him. This is not necessary. The hearing aid amplifies for him the sounds he hears. The wearing of a hearing aid will not interfere with his ability to use his eyes to learn speechreading. In fact the hearing aid can assist the process of speechreading, for audition supplements the use of the eyes. This is important when the child has a severe loss of hearing.

Your child's hearing cannot be damaged by receiving too loud sound. The aid has a maximum output or limit, which means the aid cannot pass on to the ear of the wearer any sounds louder than the ear can tolerate. This output is limited by the mechanics of the instrument. If he receives sounds or speech close to the maximum of the aid, the loudness of the sounds may frighten him. No damage can be done to the child's ear. Too loud a sound at any time can be unpleasant to him as it can be to the normal hearing child or person.

There are three types of hearing aids. One is worn on the body and is known as the body-type aid; one is worn behind the ear, or at ear level; and one is worn on the temple of eyeglasses. Only those who wear eyeglasses all the time would have the latter. For the young child the body-type hearing aid is best. These aids are more durable; they can supply more acoustic gain or power, especially necessary for the severely and profoundly deaf child; these aids can be attached more securely for the rough-and-tumble play and activities for the very young child.

More amplified power is needed during this period when the child is just learning to acquire language and speech. During these growing years he may require more than one hearing aid through breakage, loss and irreparable damage to the aid. The body-type hearing aid are often, therefore, less costly for you who has to purchase them. When your child is older or has reached young adulthood, he may change to an ear-level model, if it supplies him with the acoustic gain his hearing loss requires from a hearing aid.

All hearing aids will have a microphone for picking up the sound waves from the air; they will all have receivers to convert the amplified sound into acoustic waves which are fed into the ear of the wearer; they will all use some type of battery. The microphone of the body-type hearing aid is found at the front or face of the aid and is usually covered with a grill to protect it, as the diaphragm could be easily damaged. Sometimes there is also a clip on the face of the hearing aid. This can be used to clip the aid in the pocket of a shirt or to the dress. The small cell battery, like those used in a pencil-sized flashlight, fits into a compartment in the lower part of the back of the aid, at least that is usually where it is found. The + and − signs indicate how the batteries are to be fitted in. The plus and minus signs are also on the batteries. The plus end (positive) of the battery goes into the plus (+) end of the case. If you should put the battery in incorrectly the hearing aid will not receive the flow of power from the battery and the aid will not work. The cord, made up of many thread-like wires, is insulated to help to protect the wires from breakage. One end of the cord fits into the hearing aid case and the other end fastens to the round button-like receiver. The receiver fastens by its nub to the earpiece. The earpiece fits into the ear of the wearer. Each person has to have his own earpiece, or earmold, made to fit each ear. The earmold is usually made of a soft plastic material and should fit snugly in the ear. If it is not fitted snugly there may be a "squeal," which is annoying to the child and to you who has to listen to it as well. It has been found that it is better to use the Y-cord with a receiver and earpiece in each ear. This is a pseudobinaural hearing aid, not a true binaural aid. However, with this type of cord, both auditory neural and cerebral areas are being stimulated with the use of both ears; and the results for hearing are better than with the single cord. Many parents have reported that Johnny hears better when he is using the Y-cord than when he is using the single cord.

The tone control on the hearing aid is usually set when the aid is selected for the individual child. The volume control will have to be set by you, the parents, until the child is old enough to set it himself. Usually you will be told at what level the volume should be set for good listening. If the audiologist or the dealer does not tell you, ask what the best setting of it would be for your child. As the power of the cell battery is drained off through use, you may have to increase the volume control. Once the control is set when you put the aid on him it should be left at that as long as the child is responding as usual. To keep turning the volume up and down as the environmental sounds grow louder and weaker will destroy the effect of the aid for the child. Volume should be set at a level at which he can hear well; and he will learn to recognize sounds at this level. The speech which you hear when you listen through the hearing aid will be distorted to some extent to your ear. You must remember the aid is not a replacement for our sensitive hearing mechanism; it is only an instrument for making sounds louder; there will be some distortion in the quality of the speech you hear. The child is not aware of this distortion. He learns to recognize and place meaning to whatever he hears, when he is trained to listen.

Usually the body-type hearing aid has a telephone switch on it. Somewhere on the aid, usually at the top or on the side of the case, there is a small switch at one end of which is a T and the other M. The M stands for microphone; usually the knob of the switch is at this end (M); the T stands for the telephone switch. When grandmother phones and wants to talk to your hearing-handicapped child, push the knob to T, hold the telephone receiver upside down with the part usually held to your ear against the microphone of the hearing aid, and let him speak into the end of the telephone receiver which you always speak into. He can then carry on a conversation with grandma. Be sure to switch the knob back to M as soon as he has finished on the telephone. If you do not remember to do so, you will wonder later why he cannot hear you. He cannot receive any sound from his environment until the switch is at M (microphone).

HOW THE CHILD WEARS THE HEARING AID

For the young child the best way for him to wear the hearing aid is for you to make a pocket of flannelette the size of the hearing aid, attach tape strings to the top of this pocket so that you can tie these around his neck. Attach another set of tape strings to the bottom of the pocket for tying around his body. Let him wear the aid in front and under his shirt. Actually, it is better to have nothing covering the microphone, but, because the young child is likely to play with the instrument and/or take it apart, even lose parts, it is better to put the aid under his shirt, where he will be unable to play with it. Just remember to have as little as possible covering the aid. Do not put it under several layers of clothing. If you do, he will not receive much use from the aid.

CARE OF THE HEARING AID

Each time you put the hearing aid on your child, test it to make sure that it is working properly. You can do this in two ways; put the receiver to your own ear and listen to see if you can hear what is being said, or what you yourself are saying; or you can place the receiver against the microphone. If you get the "squeal," this is an indication that the aid is working. As the strength of the "squeal" weakens at the usual volume setting, this could mean that the battery power is being used up.

You may have operating problems with the aid, and these may

be stemming from the cord. At the point where the cord is attached to the hearing aid and the point where the receiver is fastened, there is considerable bending of the cord through daily use. One thread-like wire of the cord may break. This may cause a going-on and a going-off of the sound through the aid, because, when the broken wire connects with its part the circuit would be closed and the power would flow through it. With another movement the contact of the two wires could be broken, and the power flow from the battery would cease. If more than one wire of the cord was broken, the hearing aid would not be operating at all. You may think that you need a new battery. If you put in the aid a new battery and still the aid will not operate, you could suspect the cord. In any event, whether it was one wire or many wires of the cord that were severed, you would still have to replace the broken cord with a new one.

The channel through the earmold will become plugged with ear wax if you do not keep it clean. Unfasten the earpiece from the receiver. Using lukewarm water and a mild soap, clean the earmold. With a pipe cleaner, running it through the channel of the earpiece, you can remove wax that may be clogging the canal of the earmold. Dry the mold and attach it again to the receiver. If the child's external ear canal becomes irritated from the earpiece rubbing the skin, use some petroleum jelly or Vaseline® on the irritated area; or ask your doctor to recommend something to use.

Always remember to turn off the power when the hearing aid is not being used. Otherwise you will drain the battery power unnecessarily. It is a good habit to learn at the beginning to take out the battery from the case when the aid is not in use. If the battery should "leak" it could corrode the case. This will not happen if you make it a habit to remove the battery from the case. Keep the spare batteries in a cool, dry place. "Cool" place does not mean to store them in the refrigerator. That place is usually cold, but not *dry*.

You should carry spare batteries always when the child is away from home. The battery in his hearing aid may cease to produce power, and the child will be without his hearing aid. Be prepared for such an eventuality.

SUMMARY

In summary the hearing aid is a mechanical device which makes sounds, both sound per se and speech sounds, louder for the child. It does not give him language and speech. It is necessary for you to learn how your child's hearing aid operates. You must perform the operations until he learns how to handle the aid himself. The care of the aid is important if you are to gain maximum use from it. The hearing aid becomes your assistant in helping your child to achieve communication in the world in which he lives.

Chapter III

LANGUAGE AND SPEECH DEVELOPMENT

JAMES M. CACCAMO

THE IMPORTANCE OF SPEECH AND LANGUAGE

THE tools for communication are speech and language. For the handicapped child these present many problems. The normal language development can be a guide to you parents of the hearing-impaired. Your child may develop some language and speech, but the amount may be much less than he should have for his age level. By making a comparison with the normal landmarks you can determine if your child has a language problem. This lack of normal development could be because of the hearing loss. The following discussion may be helpful in solving some of these problems.

Before we can discuss this development we must first agree that speech and language are important. We must also agree that it is desirable for one to develop good speech and language. Everything we do in this world depends upon the development of these skills.

Those who have developed good speech and language, that is to say, those who communicate effectively through the use of speech and language, have helped shape the destiny of our whole world. People such as Winston Churchill, President John F. Kennedy and the Reverend Doctor Martin Luther King are only a few. These, as well as numerous others, through the use of speech and language, have changed not only their lives but the lives of all of us. It is with examples such as these that we are able to say: YES! speech and language are important.

It just does not happen that children learn to talk. They must be taught. It is you, the parents, who have the responsibility to help your child to talk. You, as parents, must be convinced that speech and language are important assets for your child. It is then,

24

and only then, that you will put forth a sincere effort to help your child to communicate. Remember, everything we do depends upon our ability to use and understand speech and language.

Thousands of children enter school each year with speech and language problems. You, the parents, might have been able to prevent many of these problems if you had known and understood how to help your child to talk. It is the purpose of this chapter to give to you, the parents, a better understanding of how speech and language are learned.

NORMAL DEVELOPMENT OF SPEECH AND LANGUAGE

It would be extremely helpful to define speech and language before we begin discussing their development. When talking about speech, we are talking about three major areas.

1. The first is the area of articulation. That is the production of speech sounds. Here our concern is primarily with the action of the tongue, lips, teeth, palate, and jaw as they affect the breath stream to produce the various speech sounds.
2. The second is the area of fluency. That is to say, does the child's speech flow at a rate which is considered normal? An example of speech that is not fluent is stuttering.
3. The third area is that of voice. That includes vocal pitch (the highess or lowness of the voice), vocal intensity (loudness of the voice), and vocal quality (hoarseness of the voice).

When talking about language, our interest is centered on a much broader area. We are interested in a system of symbols which is used to communicate thoughts, ideas, or feelings. This system is twofold. It entails our ability to understand language (receptive language) and our ability to use language (expressive language). This system of symbols which we call language comes in many forms. It may be spoken, written, or gestural.

Many think that teaching speech and language to a child is an easy task. Those who have attempted to teach children to talk know differently. It is truly a difficult task. A great deal of effort on your part must be put forth in order to succeed. To make the job of teaching speech and language easier, you must better understand its development.

✱ The development of speech and language begins with the infant's first cry, not his first word. Although the infant's first cry is not meaningful language, it will soon develop into meaningful language.

During the first few months, the infant's cries sound very similar. This is due to the fact that most of his crying is reflexive in nature, which means that the cries are response to a general "discomfort" and not yet differentiated. After a short period of time, the infant begins to make a relationship between the crying and the situation in which he is placed. He is now beginning to realize that when he cries, he can make someone come to his assistance to fulfill his needs and comfort him. It is at this time that mother is able to begin to distinguish between the infant's cries. She knows by the sound of the infant's cry if he is wet, hungry, hurt, etc. This is truly the beginning of the development of language. The infant is truly communicating his feelings.

In the following discussion of the normal development of speech and language, the areas of understanding language (receptive language) and the area of using language (expressive language) are presented in an attempt to give you a clearer picture of what constitutes normal speech and language development. It must be remembered that the developmental norms which will be given are average norms. That is to say, some children will develop these skills a little sooner and some a little later.

Children who are hard of hearing will develop these skills later and at a slower rate. However, with the proper teaching, they will learn.

Let us begin the discussion of normal language development at the three-month level. Prior to this time the infant's language is just beginning to develop and it is difficult to differentiate the stages of development.

Three Months

Receptive Language

At this age level the child responds to the speech of the parents by making noises. The child also responds to glances by smiling and/or cooing. The child is beginning to respond to social stimulation.

Expressive Language

At three months of age most of the child's vocalizations are reflexive in nature. They demonstrate pain, fear, pleasure, etc. At this age level, the child begins what is called the "babbling" stages. That is, the child finds that making noises is pleasurable and therefore makes noises when he is enjoying himself. These sounds which the infant makes are predominately vowels and some consonants.

Six Months

Receptive Language

At six months of age the child begins to respond to his name. This response is at a very low level; that is, the child will not respond each time you call him, but he will respond occasionally. At this level the child reacts to loud, angry and friendly tones of voice by either crying or smiling.

Expressive Language

As the child reaches the six-month level of expressive language development, he expresses his eagerness and happiness by laughing. He expresses displeasure with various tones.

Twelve Months

Receptive Language

By the time the child is one year of age he is responding to his name very definitely and is aware of the social value of speech. The child can follow simple instructions if accompanied by a gestural clue. Somewhere between the age of eight and twelve months the child begins to understand the word "no" as meaning "Stop".

Expressive Language

The child uses one or more words or fragments with meaning at this age level. His vocabulary consists of from one to five meaningful words. The child imitates sounds and sound sequences. He will frequently repeat the same syllable. For example, the child might say, "mamamamamamama." As he gets a little older, he often uses these syllables in groups of two, so that he says, "mama." Most of the child's wants are indicated by his use of pointing.

Eighteen Months

Receptive Language

As the child develops from twelve to eighteen months of age, he learns the meanings of a greater number of words. However, he sometimes gets these word meanings confused and will occasionally do the opposite of what you ask him to do. At this age level the child is very willing to play nursery games and "make believe" games. The child is able to recognize pictures of familiar persons and objects.

Expressive Language

At eighteen months of age the child's vocabulary consists of from five to twenty words. The majority of these words are nouns. The child is beginning to use sentences. The sentences are very simple in construction and consist of a noun and a verb. At approximately eighteen months the child frequently uses the word "no." The child's wants are made known through the use of speech as well as gestures. It is important here to remember that the child will not use speech to make his needs known unless you encourage and reward his attempts at verbal expression.

Twenty-Four Months

Receptive Language

As the child reaches the twenty-four-month level, he begins to listen to the meaning of words and does not get them as confused as he did six months ago. He learns to respond to specific simple verbal commands without your giving him gestural clues. Most of the child's attention is given to what is going on now. He has little idea of past and future; that is to say, he is not too concerned with yesterday or tomorrow but rather today.

Expressive Language

At two years of age the child is spontaneously forming sentences of approximately two words in length. The vocabulary is from 150 to 300 words, and the child is beginning to use pronouns but sometimes confuses these in use. At two the child is also able to name objects and suit words to the appropriate action. For example, he says, "Thank you," "Hello," etc., at the proper time. The rhythm and fluency of his speech are often poor. His vocal intensity and pitch are difficult for him to control.

Thirty Months

Receptive Language

Reaching the two-and-a-half-year level, the child understands more words and begins to understand word order, the order of words in sentences. He would not use a verb for a noun. He also can derive some meaning from this word order. The child continues to develop his understanding of specific commands and responds to more complex commands. He is beginning to learn simple time concepts and is able to understand yesterday and tomorrow as places in time. One of the most important changes which comes about in the child's learning is that at two-and-a-half years the child begins to respond to verbal rather than physical means of disciplining.

Expressive Language

By two-and-a-half-years of age, the child is able to tell his name and name facial parts such as hair, eyes, nose, and mouth. He uses sentences of approximately three words in length. The child is able to carry on a conversation with little difficulty.

Three Years

Receptive Language

The child has developed his ability to follow commands to a point where he is able to follow simple instructions and remember them until the task has been completed. His time concepts are developing even more and he is now able to understand such time areas as lunchtime, tonight, summertime, etc. The child is beginning to understand colors and by the three-year level is able to match the primary colors. A most important stage of receptive language development which comes about at approximately the three-year level is the ability to reason with the child. He has a receptive language level which now allows him to understand you when you reason with him.

Expressive Language

As the child reaches the three-year level, his expressive language abilities increase tremendously. These (expressive language) abilities continue to increase markedly throughout the remainder of the child's growth and development. Sentence length grows and sentence structure becomes more complex. The child's vocabulary at three years of age consists of 900 to 1,000 words and he may use as many as 11,000 to 12,000 words in one day. He can name familiar animals, count to five, and possibly name chief body parts.

Three and a Half Years

Receptive Language

The most noticable receptive ability at this age level is that the child will be able to understand most simple questions about his environment. Also, the child may not respond to your questions or instructions even though he understands what is expected of him.

Expressive Language

By three and a half years of age the child is using most parts of speech correctly. The pronouns which he used incorrectly at two years are now used correctly. The child can tell simple stories and his sentences are about three to four words in length. The child usually asks many "why" questions.

Four Years

Receptive Language

At four years of age the child can identify, that is point to, the primary colors. He also can identify geometric shapes such as circles, crosses, and squares. His following of commands has developed even more and by this age he can follow commands even though the object of the command is not present. By four the child can understand time concepts such as "early in the morning," "next month," and "next year."

Expressive Language

The child is still asking "why" questions at four years of age. His sentences are about five words in length. The child can count to ten and recite nursery rhymes.

Five Years

Receptive Language

By the age of five the child is able to follow three commands without interruption. He defines words in terms of use; that is, a horse is to ride on; a shoe is to put on your foot. Also, the child knows his right and left hand.

Expressive Language

The questions continue but now the child is really looking for information. At five the child's sentences are about five to six words per sentence. He can name colors, count up to thirteen, name coins, and name the days of the week.

As you can see, the child's language becomes extremely complex as we approach the five-year level. For the purpose of keeping this section as clear as possible, let us stop at this point.

Concerning these development norms, it is impossible to incorporate every speech and language developmental landmark. It is my intent to use those which would be clearest to you.

IS THERE A NEED FOR ASSISTANCE IN TEACHING MY CHILD SPEECH AND LANGUAGE?

This question is considered to be one of the most important, because in order to ask for help, you must first feel you have a need to seek assistance. It is my feeling that most parents know if their child is having difficulty in developing speech and language long before they seek professional assistance. Let me urge you to seek this professional assistance as soon as you suspect that your child might be having a problem.

If you are not sure that your child is in need of speech and language assistance, then the section of this chapter called *"Normal Development of Speech and Language"* will help you decide. Turn to the section which is closest to your child's age and attempt to determine if he can do those items which are stated. For example, if he is three years old, turn to the three-year level. Then ask, can he follow simple commands and remember them until the tasks are completed? Can he match primary colors? Can I reason with him? Can he count to five? Are his sentences three to four words in length? If you can answer "yes" to most of the questions, your child is probably developing speech and language normally. If you cannot, begin answering the questions for the next younger age. Keep working backward until you can answer "yes" to most of the items at a level. This will give you an approximate speech and language age level of development for your child.

If your child's actual age is six months or more older than his speech and language level which you have determined by using the section on *"Normal Development of Speech and Language,"* then his speech and language is probably not developing normally and he *may* have a speech and language problem. That is to say, if he is three and you answered "yes" to most of the questions at the two-year level in the *"Normal Development of Speech and Language"* section, then he may have a speech and language problem and need assistance.

Now that you have decided that your child needs professional assistance, where can you take him? If your child is of school age (we hope he is younger), then the most logical place to seek assistance would be the school. What if your child is not of school age? Then, there are several possibilities open to you.

1. If there is a university in your area you might contact them to see if they have a department which handles speech and language problems.
2. You might contact the hospital in your area to see if they have a speech pathologist or audiologist on their staff.
3. Contact the local school and explain your situation to them and perhaps they will have a speech pathologist or audiologist who can assist you.
4. You can write to the American Speech and Hearing Association, 9030 Old Georgetown Road, Washington, D.C., and ask them to provide you with a list of qualified speech and hearing professional persons in your area.

Once you have your child evaluated, it is our hope that a book such as this will assist you in helping your child learn and develop speech and language to the best of his ability.

LANGUAGE OF BEHAVIOR

One of the most important elements in teaching your child is developing adequate behavior, by setting limits with the use of both positive and negative reinforcements; that is to say, you must praise your child when he is good as well as punish him when he is not.

This section could have been titled "LOVE." Yes, giving and demanding discipline is truly love. That is love in the broadest sense of the word, which is giving of yourself to put forth time and effort to teach your child. The task of teaching children is a lifelong job. If done properly, it will bring happiness and a deeper unity and love into your home.

When teaching your child speech and language, it is important that he, as well as you, be in a state of emotional and psychological stability. This stability is brought about through love, understanding, and knowing what is expected. Yes, you *must* let your child know what you expect of him. This is done by setting limits for him. Children need to have limits even though they constantly test and fight against them.

By limits it is suggested that your child must know just what he can do and just what he cannot do. He *must* know his limits and you must tell him.

A most important aspect of setting limits is consistency. Once your child knows what you expect of him, then you must consistently demand that behavior from him. When he gives you less than what is expected, then you must discipline him. You *must* discipline him each time he gives you less than what is expected. A word of caution is necessary at this point. Parents, remember your expectations of your children must be *realistic*. For example, you would not expect your six-month-old child to walk, nor, on the other hand, would you expect a normal three-year-old to crawl. *Expectations must be realistic.*

There are many effective tools which can and must be used in teaching your child to stay within set limits. Some of them are love, praise, good example, trust, confidence, punishment, consistency, and responsibility. These tools are not listed in order of importance; if they were, they would all be number one. They are all equally important in the demand for good behavior from a child.

When you allow a child to do as he pleases, you are not teaching anything but confusion. You are showing him how little you really love him. Enforcement of good behavior patterns is not easy. It takes much time and effort to really love and teach your child limits.

What happens to a child who has been allowed to do as he pleases? Let us take you as an example. You have always done as you please and your boss tells you to do something which does not please you. You tell him you do not want to do it, and . . . .

I think this example shows what kinds of difficulties can arise if we only do as we please. So, too, with a child, many difficulties arise at home, in the neighborhood, and at school if his behavior is unrestricted. Rather than causing your child all of this difficulty, why not set limits for him and attempt to avoid these problems.

The word *discipline* always carries such a negative meaning. Let me suggest that perhaps it need not have this negative meaning. If I equate discipline with love, then perhaps the negative meaning will not be present. Remember that if you set limits for his behavior patterns, then both you and your child will be happy and more secure. Teaching a child should be enjoyable and rewarding.

SUMMARY

In this chapter, we talked about the importance of speech and language, the normal development of speech and language, identifying a need for assistance in teaching your child speech and language, and behavior. In conclusion, remember, parents, that it is your *responsibility* to teach your child. Make it an enjoyable responsibility by loving and disciplining your child. Teaching a child can be a most rewarding endeavor. If you should have difficulty, for one reason or another, teaching your child speech and language, contact a professional person for assistance. He is trained to help people, but he cannot do it unless he is asked.

Chapter IV

DAILY HOME LESSONS PLANS FOR
THE PRESCHOOL CHILD

THESE lessons have been compiled for you as a guide in assisting your child to acquire language and speech. An attempt was made to have them as practical as possible for you. If you do not finish one suggested lesson one day, do not be concerned. Just continue at the pace at which the child can follow. Take two days or more to complete one lesson and weeks to do one series if this is necessary.

These lessons are arranged and made suitable for use beginning at one year of age. The assumption is that the child has not been aware of sounds. This, then, is the beginning point. With the child who is aware of sounds around him, the beginning lessons for him would be a later one which would meet his individual requirements for developing good listening habits and for the development of speech and language. It must be kept in mind that both the use of hearing and listening are learned behaviors. They do not just happen, even with the normal hearing child. He has to learn both. But, he is able to do this with less assistance because he can hear and has the normal mechanism to do so.

The child may have ignored sounds in his home environment because they were not loud enough for him to hear, or he may have been aware of them but they held no meaning for him, and so he has learned to ignore them. The first stage, in learning to use the residual hearing available to him is to make him aware that there are sounds in his environment and that these sounds do have meaning. This becomes part of the auditory training process.

FIRST SERIES

Lesson 1

You seat the child at a child's table, and you sit opposite him or

36

beside him. It is best to have a small table at the level of which he
will be able to sit comfortably and attend to you. You can use a
drum, preferable one with a skin covering, as the pitch is lower,
and more likely to be heard by the aurally-handicapped child.
However, the tin drum can also be used. You beat the drum with
the drumstick. Have the child feel the drum while you do so. At
the same time say to the child "Hear the drum. It goes
boom-boom." Repeat this several times and then have the child
beat the drum. It may be necessary to hold the drumstick in his
hand for him. When you stop beating say, "Now it's gone." Then
let him feel the drum. You do the beating again and then say to
the child, "You beat the drum," repeating again the necessary
actions and saying, "Hear the drum, etc." You must always keep
talking to the child when you are working with him. Speak in
short simple sentences, repeating in a different way the one word
you may want him to understand. Always encourage him to watch
you while you are speaking. You could use the bell, having him
feel the vibrations and then indicating there was no sound. With
the bell it could be, "Hear the bell. It says ding-dong." Have the
child make the sound with the bell, if he can. Repetition is very,
very important throughout all the efforts you make to help your
child to use his hearing. The first lesson for the one-year-old
should last *no more* than ten minutes. The time can gradually be
increased, as his interest grows and he is able to attend longer.
Informally, you can follow the same instruction with the radio.
letting him feel the vibrations of the loudspeaker when the volume
is on loud and indicating when the volume is turned off. The piano
could be used for a variation. The record player and records would
be useful, too. The old type alarm clock or telephone could be
used. The important thing is that the child learns to know when
sound is there, and when there is no sound. In becoming aware of
sound, sound begins to have meaning. It may take days, even
weeks, before the child becomes aware of sounds and becomes
alert to them when he hears or feels those which have meaning for
him. His range of experience should increase as the days go by.
Those things which will have the most meaning for him will be
from experiences he receives naturally and daily in the home.
Much of making him aware of sounds can be done around the

home at many opportunities which present themselves naturally. All sounds must be made loud enough so that the child can hear the sound and feel the vibrations.

The lesson can be repeated during the day, once more, or several times, if you have the time and can keep his interest and cooperation.

Babble to your child – baba, mama, dada, lala. Do not use all at one time, but one time babble "baba, baba, baba"; another use "mama, mama," and so on. Encourage him to imitate you. Use babbling in your lesson with him until he begins to acquire words. Do not babble throughout the entire lesson but bring it into the procedures at appropriate places. Babble to him while you are dressing, undressing, bathing him, etc. To babble a couple of times each time is enough. Talk to him also at these times.

Lesson 2

You will proceed to Lesson 2, when the child appears to be becoming aware of sounds around him. This awareness will not be complete, when you begin this stage; he will be continually, and increasingly, becoming aware of more and more sounds as time passes and he learns to use his hearing more fully. From an awareness of sounds, he must learn to distinguish one sound from another. This is vitally important, for speech sounds differ one from the other, some only slightly, others very greatly. Take any two noisemakers that differ widely in pitch, such as a drum and a bell, with which he would be familiar from the first lesson series. Again beat the drum, saying, "The drum goes boom, boom." Ring the bell, saying, "The bell goes ding-dong." Have the child do the same, beating the drum after you and then ringing the bell when it is introduced. Repeat this several times. That will be all for this part of this lesson. Again, this should not last longer than about five minutes.

Different noisemakers can be used if he tires of the first two after a couple, or several, lessons. You could then retain one, such as the drum, and use another noisemaker, possibly a whistle (or tambourine, or clacker, or rattle, etc.). Follow the same procedures for listening as outlined above.

For the second step of the lesson, take several blue blocks, and several yellow blocks. Two or three of each are enough. Hold up a yellow block and say, "This is a yellow block. This is your block." Then give the child the yellow block and say again, "This is your yellow block." Hold up another yellow block and say, "Here is another yellow block. This yellow one is mine," and place it before you. Repeat "This is my yellow block." Follow this same procedure using the blue block, one for him and one for you. Then, proceed with the repetition of a yellow block, one for each of you, followed by another blue block, until all the blocks have been distributed between you. Now have a little game with the blocks by building the yellow upon the yellow and the blue upon the blue. As you do it, have him imitate you (you may have to take his hands and help him to build). You would say, "Let us build a tower with the blue blocks," suiting the action to the words. When this is done, "Let us push over the yellow blocks, etc.," suiting the action to the words. If he does not follow you by imitation, say, "You push over the yellow blocks," and help him if this is necessary. Do not repeat this game this lesson. Once is enough for now.

For the third part of this same lesson, have two small similar cars. When you are finished with the color game, bring on the table the cars, one at a time. "See what I have. It is a car. This is your car." Bring on the second one. "Here is my car." Push the car about the table and say, "My car goes 'beep, beep'. What does your car say?" You will answer your own question, "Beep, beep." You may have to place his hand on the car and help him to push it back and forth and supply the vocalization for him. Try to keep him imitating your actions, and discourage him from initiating his own play at this point. Do not prolong this game for longer than a few minutes this first time. You may have to arouse his interest and develop the idea of imitation.

For this lesson and all the following ones, the child should be seated at the small table with you sitting opposite him, where he can see your face clearly. To encourage him to watch your face, you should hold up in line with your lips the object of which you are talking. With practice he will learn to associate the lip movements with the object and thus learn to use his eyes to assist his hearing.

The whole lesson should not be longer than fifteen to twenty minutes at this point. You should be able to repeat the whole lesson again next day with the same material. You might be able to use the material for several days, before he tires of it. You must remember that repetition is very important. He must hear the same words with the same material for many times before he begins to understand what is being said to him.

Large plastic or wooden beads could be used instead of the blocks, or later these could be substituted for the blocks. Whatever is used for the play with the objects should be something the child will see or use in his everyday experiences and he will have the opportunity to hear their names often in a natural way. Whatever noisemakers are used, they should be quite different in pitch, one from the other for these lessons.

Wherever possible always transfer the learning situation into everyday natural experiences. This will broaden his knowledge of language. It will be very slow, but the constant exposure to the language in situations with which he becomes familiar speeds the learning process.

The learning of colors can continue informally around the house when the child is with you and you are administering to his wants and pleasures. When giving him jelly beans, hand him a yellow one, and say, "Here is a yellow jelly bean" (or a 'yellow candy'). (The correct name for everything would be preferable, so that he has only one name at a time to learn.) Do this with a couple of colors at a time only. M & M's® could be also used. When he is out in the car, and the car horn is blown, draw his attention to the sound by saying, "The car says 'beep, beep," or whatever sound you are going to associate with a car. You must be consistent in the use of the same word for the same object or action in the same situation. As he learns, different words can be used for new associations with the same object or similar objects. Right now he is not ready for this.

Lesson 3

Begin these lessons when the child shows some signs of

mastering the previous material, not necessarily having learned to do all, but to have learned to do at least some of it. Just do not proceed too quickly.

Again, using the drum and the bell, you make the sound of each and have him do the same thing each time after you. He should be able to do this by himself now. That is, you should not have to take his hand and put him through the motion of beating the drum, etc. Then, using large buttons, ones he cannot put in his mouth and swallow, or wooden beads, or even small stones that you may have collected, you drop one of these in a tin can, or carton, or a small box (any such container), as you beat the drum once loudly. You may have to do this again to show him. Then have him try to imitate you by dropping a button in the tin while you beat the drum. He should see you beating the drum. You may have to put the button in his hand and indicate to him that he is to drop the button in the can when you beat the drum. You may even have to take his hand and help him to drop the button into the can. Repeat this several times. Each time a different button must be dropped into the can. Repeat the performance yourself, by dropping a button in the tin, if you feel this might help the child to imitate you more easily. Each time you do this you say, "Hear the drum. Put the button in the can when you hear the drum go 'boom, boom.' " (He will not necessarily understand what you are saying at this point, but he will soon learn that you have some meaning for him when you vocalize.) Before each sounding of the noisemaker, you say, "Listen!" and point to your ear and assume a listening attitude yourself. Each time you beat the drum, you say, "Listen to the drum. Listen." When you have done this several times, do the same with the bell or whatever you are using. This first step should take no more than five to seven minutes. Do not prolong this stage at any time, or the child will become bored with it, and you will defeat the purpose for which you are using it. Even though nothing is learned, you still do not prolong this activity. This will be the beginning step of learning to listen and to discriminate, or distinguish, one sound from another. To be able to distinguish one speech sound from another is very vital in the learning of language and speech.

Again use two cars, maybe of a different color and size from those used in the second lesson series. Your cars should be similar to the ones he has. He is given one at a time as you name each. This time add two boats. Give him one at a time as with the cars. The boat says, "PPPPPP" or "Put-put-put." (In using such vocalizations, you are setting the stage for the eventual recognition of speech sounds.) Have a game with these objects, trying to get him to imitate whatever you do with each in turn. (You might have a dish or pan of water in which the boats could sail.) You must end the play; he should not. The play should not last longer than about ten minutes − shorter, if he shows signs of becoming tired or bored with the game. End the play by asking him to give you each car, then each boat. You should pick up your car and say, "Give me the (or your) car"; at the same time you hold out your hand and point to your open palm that you want him to put his car in your hand (or give it to you). You may have actually to take up his car and to put it in your hand, if he still cannot understand what you are trying to say to him. Use the same procedure with the boat. First, however, give him the opportunity of doing it himself, if he understands. Do not *expect* him at first to understand; but he might surprise you and imitate your actions. (You must remember that imitation is the beginning of the process of association, which is learning.) You talk to him each time you want him to do something and supply the appropriate actions to give meaning to your words. Avoid gestures as much as possible. Gestures are more easily learned then speech.

For the step of the lesson described above two objects are enough to use the first time. You may choose whatever two objects that you know your child will have the most experience with in everyday living. Again, whenever you are outside the home and see any of the things with which you have been working, for example a boat, always draw his attention to it, so that he learns to recognize the real object when he sees one. Always make sure that he can see your face when you speak to him, and he can see what you are talking about.

This type of lesson will be repeated over the following weeks until he shows some mastery of the material and ideas involved in the lesson. You should vary the material when there are signs that the child's interest is waning. Fresh materials can be replaced by the things he has had before, when interest in the newer materials gives away; that is, use the things you have used for previous lessons. Much of the success for any lesson depends upon the interest and enthusiasm you put into the lesson yourself. If you are not interested, or have other things on your mind, how can you expect your child to be interested? His responses will often be a reflection of your own.

Lesson 4

Every lesson now should begin with an exercise in sound discrimination. You are still working with gross sounds, that is, two sounds that are dissimilar or far apart in pitch. After some practice responding to the sounds, and when he is able to use his eyes and his ears meaningfully, he then is taught to respond to sound by ear alone.

Now the first step is to have him respond to the drum as he was doing previously. Have him respond to the bell in the same way. That is he puts a bead in the box when he can see you beat the drum, etc. Then, you beat the drum under the table; it will not matter if he can see your arm movements at this point. You talk to him about what you are doing as you have been telling him and remind him to listen. For example, you will say, "Beat the drum. The drum goes boom boom. Listen." You will do the same thing with the bell or whatever you are using. You will have him respond with a button or a bead, or whatever you are using, as he has been doing when he could see and hear what was happening as you beat the drum. Right now he has to depend upon his ears mainly. Repeat your actions with the drum a couple of times. Do this with the other noisemaker which you are using. You may have to show him at first by your actions that you want him to respond in the same way as he has responded in the previous lesson when he hears the sound. The first time you may have to put the bead in the box as you beat the drum or ring the bell out of sight. This is a new experience for him. Again this part of the lesson should not last any longer than five minutes of the lesson time.

The color activity could make use of the formboard, or pegboard, or peg and ring set. You take the forms from the board in front of you, one at a time, name each as you do this and give each to him. Then, point to each matching color on the formboard, saying again, "This is blue, etc." When all the pieces are removed from the formboard, you follow this by placing the board in front of him. You point to the color on the formboard where you want him to put back the corresponding color form. Assist him to do this, if he cannot do it himself. At the same time talk to him about the name of the colors, each time one is handled. For example, you say, "This is blue." At all times the child is encouraged to repeat the name regardless of how much or how little of the word he gets correct. A "b" or "oo" for blue is still a good attempt at this point. If the child can place the color form back into the correct space in the formboard when you ask him, let him do this by himself. Indeed, let him always do everything which he understands and can do without your help. Make him dependent upon himself to do the things he can do. Never discourage independence, but guide it into the channels for learning.

Introduce the objects that you are now going to use. Say, "This is the car. This car is yours. This car is mine." Hold up the car toward your face so the child can see the object and what you are saying at the same time. Follow this procedure with two or more objects. These can be objects of transportation, animals, things such as furniture, food, drinks, or persons. When you each have three identical objects, institute a spontaneous play game with them, talking simply about the actions and the objects. For example, you could say, "My car can say 'beep, beep.' What does your car say? Is this like daddy's car? My car goes very fast." You must remember to talk about the cars on a level at which a small child would naturally and normally be interested. This time teach him the meaning of "Show me the ———." You say, "Show me the ———," by pointing to your object, for example, the car. Then, take his hand when you say, "Show me the *car,*" and point his finger to the same object. Go through this same procedure for all of the objects. Then repeat this with the objects in random fashion. You finish this part of the lesson by saying, "Give me ———," and hold out your hand for each. You put each object away when he gives it to you.

You finish the lesson by having him listen to the music (records are good) and have him clap time to the music. You also clap, and let him imitate you. Stop the music and stop the clapping at the same time. If he continues to clap, put his hands by his sides and say "The music is all gone." You then start the music again and start clapping. A child's record player and nursery records are useful for this. Choose the records that do have a rhythm to them. Since this may be a new experience to him, you may have to take his hands and clap them for him. If you can sing, you could take him on your lap, and sing to him while you clap his hands. A nursery song could very well be used for this, too. He could sit at the table as he had done for the rest of the lesson, and respond to the music there. However, by standing up, or sitting on your lap, this would add some variety to the lesson.

Again, this lesson would be repeated for as long as you felt it was necessary to do so, varying the material somewhat from day to day, as you felt this to be necessary in order to maintain the child's interest. The child should show some mastery of the ideas involved in the lesson before you go on to the next lesson series. Material should be varied as needed, and making use of whatever material you have available. Since one lesson overlaps another, there should not be the necessity for too much repetition of each lesson after the third one, or after this one. But, again, it would depend upon the progress the child was making, whether or not you would proceed to the next lesson series after this series has been used for a few times.

Lesson 5

The progression in the series could follow fairly quickly now, as some sound recognition will have been established. But do not hasten on to another series, if the child is not ready for it.

As always there should be the sound-listening "starter" for the lesson to set the tone for the rest of it by listening and discriminating sounds. In this series, using two noisemakers, have the child respond once to each when he can see the object, and then you go behind him, make the sound of the same noisemaker and indicate he must respond by placing a block in the box. Do the same with each noisemaker. He must have no visual clues this time. Repeat this performance as often as you feel is necessary at this point. Do not get so close behind him that he can feel the vibrations from the object or so that he can feel the air movements caused by the motions you make with the noisemaker. You can have him cover his eyes, turn his back to you, or you can turn his chair so that his back will be to you while you make the sound with the object. These suggestions could add some variation to the lesson procedures. Now, place the objects on the table before him, have him close his eyes, and you make the sound of one of the noisemakers. Then ask him, "Which one did you hear?" You are likely to have to repeat the words and maybe even have to point to the right object yourself. Repeat the whole procedure until he understands what you want him to do or how you want him to respond. In other words, for the first couple of times you use this procedure, you may have to give the answer yourself by pointing to whichever noisemaker was used. Be brief with this part as usual. (The last part of this procedure — placing the objects on the table and having him close his eyes, while you make the sound — could be used the second or third lesson of the series instead of on the first day.)

For a color activity you could have him thread beads. Use only the primary colors — red, blue, yellow. You would say, "Put on (the string) the red bead." If he cannot choose from the nine beads before him, then you hold up the same color from your pile. Repeat the request until all the beads have been threaded. You could also string your beads, too, imitating his actions. However, first let him choose the color you ask for before you thread your bead. Let him choose the correct color himself and only help him when he cannot do this alone. If he can choose by the process of elimination let him do it this way at this time. (Later, do not let him choose by the process of elimination.) Later he should be able to make the choice on the first try. If he does not choose the correct bead, you then must choose it for him. If guessing goes on and on, he will never learn to listen and to respond correctly. You are, of course, talking to him about the colors, and trying to get him to imitate the name of the color that you are saying.

For the language part of the lesson you could use dolls, or toy people, and introduce a play session for action words such as "walk" or "run." Have the dolls do these actions. "See the doll walk (run). Can your doll walk?" He should imitate your doll's actions with the doll he has. That is, you have your doll walk and have him make his doll do the same. Then you and he could get up from the table and walk, then run.

For the musical part use a record in march time. Have the child march with you, then walk with you, and finally have him run with you to the music. Do not move too far from the source of the music; that is, keep within hearing distance of the music for him. You may find that you can only accomplish one of these in a lesson. Make certain that he connects his activity with the music.

Throughout the lesson, and at all other times, keep using "Listen," and pointing to your ears, and to his ears; and "watch," indicating your eyes. If there is enough repetition he will get the idea of it eventually, if he does not get the idea sooner.

The length of the lesson should now be one-half hour. To prolong it more when he has had this amount of concentration defeats the purpose of his and your efforts. Concentration is tiring and so is listening when one has not been doing it.

For the language part various common action words should be learned by the child; and that means you must teach the child these words. These should be words that he will hear and use often in his everyday experiences. The following are some of these words: sit down, stand up, jump, go, come, eat.

Lesson 6

Continue with the discrimination of gross sounds. You should vary the noisemakers that you use. Eliminate the visual clues and have him listen only. That is, there should be no need of him to respond first to the noisemakers when he can see them. By having him listen and discriminate sounds, remember you are setting the time for the rest of the lesson. As soon as he shows signs of really listening go on to the next part of the lesson. However, as before, do not prolong this part more than the usual five minutes. At this stage begin to condition him to respond to speech. By imitation show him that, when you say "Go," he will put a bead in the box. Have him do this a number of times when he can watch you, or can speechread, as well as listen. When he is ready to listen without looking at you, cover your lips with your hands and have him respond appropriately. You will likely need to take several lessons to accomplish all of this. This should form a part of the first five minutes, not in addition to it.

For the color activity you could get a small twig of a tree, stand it in plasticiene or clay, and pretend it was a tree. Then, using colored paper, or plain white paper that you have colored and which you have cut into the shape of red, green and yellow leaves, have him put one leaf at a time on the tree, after each has been named by you and by him. He can attach these to the tree with Scotch® Tape put on each leaf; or you could use Sticky Tac.® (This Sticky Tac can be bought at the dime store or a bookstore.) You will likely have to show him what you want him to do the first time; you may even have to assist him. However, help him only when he cannot do by himself what you want him to do. Always let him do the things he can do himself and praise him for his efforts no matter how crudely they are performed. As with every lesson the appropriate words should be used throughout the activity. For example, "Put your blue leaf on the tree." You may have to have a set of the leaves, too, so that you can use the matching technique the first round or two. You match your leaves to his, if he can choose the right colored leaves. Try to get him to recognize the color you want by a trial-and-error method from the child himself. This is appropriate at this stage. "Where is your yellow leaf?" If he chooses the wrong one, just say, "No, that is not the yellow. I want the yellow one." When he is successful, "Yes, that is the yellow one. Good." A clap of your hands, and an expression of pleasure are adequate praise for him. If he cannot give you the correct colored leaf, you can pick it up and say, "This is the red leaf" and then have him put it on the tree.

The language activity should still be in the form of toy objects — people, animals, food, furniture, clothing, transportation vehicles, etc. He should be matching objects fairly well by now. That is, he should be choosing the same one as you when you pick up one object, or whatever you do with it, and when you name it.

Now begin giving out only one object of each group (vehicles, for instance) and trying to get him to institute the desired play at your request alone. "Make the car go 'beep, beep' " by pretending to push the horn. You would have had practiced with this previously. Whatever you request of him now would be activities that he has already learned with you. His responses will be trial and error at first, when he must depend on his own listening to help himself. You must go slowly and encourage at all times. Do not ask him to do more than a couple of things by himself at first. The number of requests will be increased as he gains experience in learning to depend upon his listening. Of course, at the beginning you may have to point to, or pick up, whatever the object is and show him how to do the activity you want him to do; but you should always have him repeat your performance. Reinforce every action, so that auditory memory will be built up and his experiences will increase in number.

The musical activity should follow as usual. Records are most versatile. With a nursery rhyme you can say the words, while he watches you and he listens to the music. You and he will both clap your hands.

Repeat this series as often as you need to do but vary the materials when the child shows a lack of interest for what you have been using. After the fresh materials become boring, go back and use what you had been using with previous lessons. Children do not tire of the same material too readily, if the use you make of them is interesting to them, and this becomes your task. Again, everything that is done must have the appropriate words supplied by you each time, whether it is during a lesson or in everyday living.

Lesson 7

For the first step in this series, choose two noisemakers that are fairly close together in pitch. As an example you might use two drums, or two bells. These must not be so close in pitch that the child cannot recognize the difference. Have him listen and make the noise with each when he can see them. Then have him turn his back, while you produce the noise of one. He must turn and point to, or pick up, or show you in some way, which object made the noise. Do not reinforce guessing by allowing him to make too many guesses. You can stop guessing by showing him yourself which noisemaker was used when he cannot identify the correct object himself. Then repeat the whole procedure. There may be much trial and error at first; and again he may be able to identify each sound as he hears it the first time. If he is learning to develop good listening habits, he will be able to follow your instructions quite readily, although he may not understand them exactly. Use the "Go" game also; but this time stand some distance behind him when you say "Go." Have him respond by putting pegs in a pegboard, or some such activity.

For a color activity have a large picture tree, the outline of which you have drawn on wrapping paper, or on plain white paper. Have colored birds cut from colored paper, or outlined birds traced on white paper which you have then colored with crayons. Have the birds the colors you want to use for the lesson. Following the same procedure, have him name the color of the bird each time, if he can name it himself; otherwise you name it and have him say the name after you. Then, have him put each bird on the picture tree with Sticky Tac,®after he has named each color. When all the birds are on the tree (six to eight birds, using three colors should be sufficient), have him take a bird from the tree. For example, "Give me the red bird." Do this until all the birds have been taken from the tree.

You can begin to use pictures for the language activity. You can choose the picture objects, the names of which he has learned when you were using the toys. Do not use any more than three or four pictures. You should not need a set of the same pictures; one set of pictures for him is all that you require. Have a play activity with these as you did with the toys. Fly the airplane and say "ZZZZZ" or whatever sound you have been associating with an airplane. Always use sounds that are close to, or the same as, the real thing. Try to get as much spontaneous speech as you can from him. However, you must not be upset if you get little from him. There is a wide variation in times when children begin to use speech and the amount they use.

Speaking should always give him pleasure. You should finish the language activity by asking him to paste the car in his scrapbook, which might be begun now. Say, "Let us paste the car in your book." You should have the paste ready for him and help where necessary; but do not give him help when it is not necessary; let him do what he can by himself, even though the results are crude. If he chooses the wrong picture, you say, "No, that is not the car. Which one is the car? That is right. That is the car." Follow the same procedure with each of the pictures.

For the musical activity the piano could be used, if it is available. Play a simple march tune and have him march. Another time you could have him skip to an appropriate tune. Another time you could choose a musical composition (song) that could be used for running. The same activity could be followed by using the record player and the appropriate music.

Incorporated into one lesson of the series you could have the child identify objects by the sense of touch. This could be used at various times for variation in your lessons. You would place a number of toys or real objects − not too many (8-10) − in a large paper bag. He must put in his hand and pick out the object you ask him to choose. He must do this by touch alone; that is he must not peer into the bag to see what he is picking up. You say, "Give me the spoon." "Give me the dog." Do this until most of the articles have been recognized correctly. The last two or three objects could be chosen by guesswork, if he does recognize each by the sense of touch; so you need not have him choose everything that is in the bag.

A useful suggestion might be for you to remember when you are buying toys for your child at Christmas, his birthday, etc., to buy them with the idea of the use you could make of them during his lessons. They should be things which he would enjoy too. Child guidance toys are extremely useful and are fun for him as well.

Woolworth, Kresges and toy departments of stores can supply you with many simple things you could use. The toys you buy need not be indestructible or expensive.

Creative Playthings Incorporated and Sifto are firms where material can be bought. Maico Hearing Aid Company, Minneapolis, Minnesota, is the source for the record and manual for WHAT'S ITS NAME?.

For later use, begin to cut out from magazines and collect the pictures you can use for the child's lessons, and for use in his scrapbook, when this is begun.

Another suggestion is to have for yourself a progress book in which you record and keep all the child's speech efforts. At first it may be only "He said 'b,b,b,' several times today." Or, "He said 'ah' when he wanted a drink of water." Or, "He said 'boo' after me today." Or, "He said 'oo' (or blue) by himself." Always keep the date when you are recording the efforts. This will help you to realize that progress is being made although it does not appear so in everyday activities. It will assist you, too, from becoming discouraged, which you very easily can do. Remember failure will be only when you do not try and persist in your effort to help your child. As you help him he will learn although you may not readily see the fruits of your labors.

Lesson 8

For the first stage of this series continue to use noisemakers that are more nearly similar. You can vary your choice of noisemakers from day to day if you wish or if you need to do so to keep up the child's interest. For a variation, after he has listened to the sounds briefly, you go behind his chair with two or three noisemakers and make a sound with one of these. He must tell you by pointing to it the one which made the sound. Repeat the same procedure using a different one of the group to make the sound. Repeat the procedures a couple more times for practice even though he was correct in his response each time. You stand far enough behind his chair so that he cannot feel the vibrations or the air movement when you make the noise with the object. Gradually increase the distance from him and make the sound. You will do this when he has been able to listen and respond to the sounds for a lesson or two at a closer distance. Now you could also use the "Go" game in the same way. You could have him turn around toward you when he heard you say "go." Speak "go" in a normal voice. Sometimes you could say it in a quiet voice. For a quiet voice the distance behind him might have to be less than for a normal voice.

For a color activity you could have him choose the colored paper balloon you want to use in the lesson. You could have him put each on the flannelboard, after you had asked for it or, using Sticky Tac®put each on a plain piece of plywoodboard you keep for such purposes. (Sticky Tac could be purchased at Woolworth's or any school supply store.) For a variation of this, for one lesson, you could have some actual ballons and have him make the choice of color for which you ask. He could blow up each balloon as he chooses it. You may have to help him to do this. Then, ask him to "Put the yellow balloon in the box (on the big table, on the chair, etc.)." You could invent any number of simple games for your child, and he would enjoy them and learn from them.

In the third step of this lesson series, you could use pictures, giving each to him as you name each. Have him also name each after you. If he can name the picture object without your help, let him do so. Those picture objects you use could be what he would see in his daily life or with which he has often experienced. The objects could be farm animals; they could be pets, etc. If they are farm animals, each picture animal might be put into a barn, which you could readily construct, in outline form, from construction paper, or even newspaper. (Construction paper could be purchased at any store having school supplies.) Then each animal could be taken out again and put to pasture, which could be enclosed with a fence. When it was night the animals would have to go to their home in the barn again. Children have a great deal of imagination; make use of it, when they understand what is being done and said. Associate these activities and things with the real objects later in the day, or whenever it is possible to do so. You could sometimes make use of the toy material in conjunction with the picture material. Use all in as many ways as you possibly can do. You would, of course, be naming, talking about the actions, colors and size of objects in the course of many lessons. You could contrast big and small for one lesson, for another soft and hard, etc. You could talk about the big dog and the small (or little) dog. You might have one lesson (or maybe two) on the bat, ball, glove and such equipment for a ball game and indicate the use of each. Then have him try to tell you what each is, and how it is used; or he could act out how each is used, at the same time telling you the name of each. He might say "Ball. Throw." That would be acceptable. He would be putting more than one word into use at one time; and this would be the forerunner of the sentence. Follow this, if you can, that day or the next with an actual game of batting the ball between the two of you outside. The game would be very simple in scope. You could follow this pattern for many things that are natural to his and to your environment.

Follow a similar procedure for the musical activity. Reinforce the rhythm patterns by clapping, tapping, marching, running, skipping, or whatever you may choose to do. The child must always be close enough to the music so that he can hear it. If he gets too far away, the activity will have no purpose for him and your attempts to develop the rhythmic patterns for speech. Nursery rhymes (recorded) could still be used for just listening, while you say, or sing the words clearly, and clap out the rhythm pattern at the same time. He should be encouraged to say a word here and there or to follow throughout if he can do so. He can imitate your clapping rhythm at least. You should not expect him to say the words.

To encourage him to vocalize or to help him to improve his vocalizations, take his hand and have him feel your throat and jaw as you say the word. Immediately place his hand on his own throat and jaw and have him try to repeat the movement and the word. You will, of course, have to say it first for him to imitate you. It does not matter if he says the word correctly or not at this point; as long as he tries to imitate you, that is all you should want. If he does do well in the imitation of the word, that is good; but do not *expect* him to do well. The child may object to this procedure. If he does, desist from the use of it for the present; try it again at some later time. Some children will not tolerate this tactile method at all. As he grows older, he may become more amenable to the use of the method if he still needs it.

Lesson 9

Now you increase the number of noisemakers of similar pitch to three or four. After he has listened to them briefly, first while he can see them, then have him go three to six feet away from the table and keep his back to it. (You will have to take him to where you want him to stand and to show him what he is to do the first time.) You make the sound with one of the noisemakers on the table — bell, drum, whistle, clacker — and then indicate to him that he is to come to the table and pick out the object with which you made the sound. He may understand what you want him to do just by telling him. If he does understand this is fine. Remember to give him the chance to understand first without your assistance if he can do so. But, always help him with the answer if he cannot get it by himself. You could also use the "Go" and "Stop" game. When you say "Go," he must get up and walk somewhere in the room, and when you say "stop," he must stop walking and stand where he is. You could substitute the words "run" and "walk" sometimes. Do not do this activity more than twice in one lesson.

For color variation you could go back to the colored formboard, or pegboard and practice learning color recognition with one of these. You could make a colored formboard or pegboard, if you have the tools to do so. Make a square, circle, triangle, rectangle, diamond-shape, etc., and paint them the colors you want. You could use an ordinary checkerboard and use colored circles of paper to place on this. You could ask him to put a red circle on a black square of the board, etc. At all times now he must follow instructions which you give him. You accept as close to a correct response as he can make. When he makes an incorrect response, or an inappropriate response, this must be corrected immediately. "No, that is not a red one. This is the red circle." Or, "Yes, that is the red one." if he, on a second try, gives the correct response.

The language activity could be based on dressing and undressing a doll and naming the clothes each time. (Use a girl doll for the girls and a boy doll for the boys.) You instruct him to take off "Ken's" coat, or shoes, etc., or "Sally's" dress. You might even take the doll swimming wearing his swimsuit in the washbasin or sink, if the doll is the type that can go in the water. He will be learning the names of the clothing with which he should now be familiar and how to dress and undress, put off and put on.

Another game could be "Ken" eating a meal, naming some of the foods; another time "Ken" could be made to sit on a chair, sit at the table, listen to the radio or television, go to bed. This could all be done with toy furniture. This should be followed with the child doing the same things for himself when it is appropriate times to do these things in his daily routine.

For the musical activity you could play a simple tune on a xylophone, or on the piano if you are musical. It could be as simple as "doh, ray, me, fa, so, la, ti, doh," taken one at a time on the xylophone. The child would say each with, or after, you in rhythm time; then slowly repeat the whole scale. You would not do all this in one lesson. You would gradually build up the scale over several lessons. If you do not have a xylophone, you could use the piano in the same way, starting at middle C. You could also sing the scale without an accompanying instrument. If neither of these two instruments are available, then use the record player and nursery rhymes, singing or saying the words in time to the music. The child must always listen and respond actively to the activity. If he does not have to respond actively, he is not likely to listen actively, and any interest there may have been will quickly wane. And the activity will have no purpose.

Lesson 10

By now the child should be able to discriminate the sounds of similar pitch at farther distance, as far as his unaided or aided hearing will enable him to hear. Listening habits should be established, but they will not necessarily be completed. Continue with similar activity for responding to the noisemakers as he has been doing in the last series. This is still used to get him in the mood to listen well to the rest of the lesson. A xylophone could be used for variation. While he is watching, you hit two bars and see if he can produce tones you played. When he has mastered two, use three bars and up to four if he can eventually handle that many. You will have to keep reminding him to listen carefully. WHAT'S ITS NAME record and manual could now be used. The child must associate the recorded sound correctly with the picture supplied in the manual. When he is wrong, he must be shown the correct response or answer.

The color activities should include red, yellow, blue, green, orange, and purple. He should be able to recognize and use three or four at one time. You could have a paper doll with different colored shoes, dresses, socks, coats, hats, etc., and ask the child to put on the blue dress, the red shoes, the green hat, etc. This could also be a learning situation for you to teach the child a good taste in color combinations for carry-over into her, or his, own choice of clothing, You could have paper square, circles, etc., and ask the child to color each the color you request, with him using crayons; or you could have outline drawings of the clothing and have him color each piece before putting on the doll, which could be a paper one.

The language activity might include the setting of a table using pictures materials; or toys could be used. (for lunch, breakfast, or dinner.) The appropriate speech vocalization and actions should be used. You could use toy dishes, spoons, knives, and forks and wash and dry these, using actual water, dish cloth and towel; the dishes then should be put away in the cupboard. The lesson could include the preparation of actual food such as peeling a potato (be careful he does not cut himself with the knife – give him a dull one, and he can still do a crude job), shelling peas etc., and putting into a pot to cook – on a toy stove, if one is available. Outdoor activities could be used. Whatever the activity it should encompass a complete activity that does take place in his everyday environment.

For the musical activity choose from the various activities suggested before or invent one of your own. You might be able to teach him a line or two of some simple song that he could sing with you. This would be possible if he were using some speech by now. He may only say a word of the song here and there, but as long as he was producing some rhythmic pattern, the effort would be good.

Number counting could be introduced now. Use three jelly beans, or apples, oranges, pebbles, buttons, etc., and have him count these with you. After some practice, give him one jelly bean to eat, if he can count that without your help, two when he can count to two, and three when he can count to three. Do not give him one (two) to eat every time, or he will expect this — and that would be teaching a habit you would not want him to acquire. Occasionally, giving a certain number of jelly beans could be a reward. When he has counted three apples, give him one apple to eat. Indicate he is getting "one apple." Marbles, beads, blocks, etc., could also be used for counting. Transfer counting to other things he sees, or handles, or has, in the everyday life around him.

The first ten series of lessons might take only six months, or they might take a year or more to cover them all. No time limit should be set. They are proposed for building the foundation for good listening and learning to understand or to give meaning to the sounds around him, sounds per se, speech sounds, and to build a usable vocabulary. The more formal lesson methods and procedures are included in the next series, which should lead him up to readiness for nursery or kindergarten.

By the end of the first series he will have, or should have, some language and speech which he understands and can use in appropriate situations without stimulation from you. The speech will not be perfect, nor can you expect this, for the normal hearing child's speech at this learning level is not perfect. He may have only words to express himself, or he may be able to use words in combination, but not necessarily in complete sentences.

SECOND SERIES

Lesson 11

By the time the first series are completed, the child should have some foundation for language and speech. If the child is only hard of hearing and has some language and speech when his first lessons are to begin, the lessons might possibly start at this point. Discrimination of gross sounds might still be necessary, however. For the first step of the lesson you would have to go back to lesson 3 or 4 of the first series. But the color work, language and vocabulary building might be begun at this level.

The routine for the lesson should be established, if you have done the first series, and now you would only have to prepare the lesson material before the lesson. However, if you are going to begin at this point for the first time with the child, then you would have to set up a routine and have him get used to it, before you would make much progress. You could establish the routine and still use this lesson series; do only one or two parts of the lesson at the first sessions and gradually increase the number of activities in succeeding lessons until you have covered the whole lesson.

As it will be throughout the series, the first step of any lesson henceforth will be only indicated, as the procedures will aready have been established. (If you are just beginning, note the procedures to use by reading instructions of lessons 2, 3, or 4.) You can use sounds that are of similar pitch, recorded sounds, speech sounds, or words for the child to learn to recognize and to discriminate one from the other when he listens to them.

The language part will now be formed around a specific topic for each series (see Apendix C). The first unit will be on the family. The child will have heard you name the various members of your family before, but now you will concentrate on each person — mother (mummie), father (daddy), or whatever are the natural names you use in the home, names of brothers and sisters, grandmother and grandfather, aunts and uncles, and cousins. Do not bring in the names of relatives unless the child is likely to be seeing them almost daily or weekly. Actual photographs, or pictures of the people or toy people could be used to represent the persons in the family group. The carry-over should be made to the actual persons each time the child is with them. The language would be built around the activities of the family, after the child has begun to recognize the names of the various people. One lesson could be on the family having a meal at home. Here you would make use of the food eaten at one meal, the table, chairs, setting the table, putting on the table the knives, forks, spoons and so on. You could go through all the procedures using toy table, chairs, dishes, etc.; you could do the same thing with pictures, if you had these. What I have suggested would be too much material for one lesson. Break the material down into two or three lessons — or more if you felt this was necessary. The real thing could be enacted when you are actually setting a table and preparing the food. This lesson might be more interesting for a girl than for a boy, but he should be exposed to it, too.

You would not necessarily have to begin with the family unit. If he knew all the material covered above, it would be pointless to waste time on things which he already knew well. If he did not know the names, actions of descriptive words related to family life well, it would be wise to still cover the material; just spend less time on it.

The color activity should be based on the activity used for the language material. That is the colors used should be based on the lesson theme. You could have a red apple, a yellow lemon; a blue flower for the table, a white table cloth, etc. You would concentrate for the first part on the primary colors – red, blue, yellow – until he has learned these fairly well. Again the color objects could be cut out and placed in the real or picture dish for fruits or a vase for the flowers for the table. Do not be concerned with the name of the flower, just the color of it.

The musical theme could be learning a line or so of a song and repeating and adding to it each lesson, if the child can do this. Or you and he could listen to nursery rhymes and learn to sing these from recorded music. If you cannot sing, saying the words in rhythmic time would be appropriate. The piano could be used in the same way.

The musical activity would not vary too much from the previous lessons, unless you could invent something new, as learning to play a simple tune on the xylophone.

The lesson series could include the enactment of the family activities on a picnic; one day the lesson could involve the preparation for the picnic; another lesson could be playing out the picnic. These activities could follow, or precede, an actual family picnic to the park or river.

Another lesson could be the family at the zoo. You would concentrate on the things the family would do, but not the names of the animals the child saw at the zoo; learning the names of the animals would come in a later lesson on animals. The animals seen would be named, of course, but the concentration of animal name-learning would not be done at this time.

Another theme could be the family weeding the garden, if this was appropriate to the child's everyday experiences. You could name the various vegetables and fruits grown, if any are grown. You could be planting the garden instead of weeding it. Any activity that the family performed together could form the unit for any one lesson.

The number of lessons that you had with any one theme could be up to you. Always base your color activity on that involved in the theme of the lesson. For example, you would talk about and use in your lesson in the garden the green onion, yellow bean, red tomato, etc.

Language themes and language activities are listed in Appendix C at the back of the book. You need not take them in the order given, but, you must remember that whatever material you use, it should be tied in as closely as possible with the child's everyday experiences. The daily experiences will give plenty of opportunity for the repetitions of names and actions. It is through hearing and seeing the word spoken many times that the child learns to recognize each word when he hears or sees it. Thus his vocabulary grows.

Lesson 12

For this lesson series, the theme could be *the person.* One part could be learning the parts of the body – eyes, nose, mouth, tongue, hair, face, teeth, arm, leg, body, feet, fingers, thumb. Another part could be about the clothing worn indoors; the last part on the clothing worn outdoors – first those worn in warm weather, second those worn in cold weather. Step one of the lesson would still be the one on the discrimination of finer sounds – noisemakers of similar pitches – with the distance as far away from the child as he can hear; or you can have him discriminate between two vowels (*ah and ee*). You could have him put a marble in a box when he hears you say "ah," and a block in the box, when you say "ee." (You would, of course, have to take a lesson or two to teach him how you expected him to respond with two different responses to two different sounds. You could use two different responses with the noisemakers as well.)

For a suggested color activity for the first part, you might make an outline of a hand on brown wrapping paper and have him paste on the fingers in the three primary colors (red, blue and yellow) after he had named them by himself, or with your help (if this is absolutely necessary). Always give him the assistance he needs before he becomes frustrated or develops a habit of guessing. Remember to let him do the activities himself, if he can do this. Or, for the activity, you could have an outline of a face and have him paste on the blue eyes, the red tongue, and the yellow hair. For another time, the paper doll, or a real doll, could be dressed in a blue dress, yellow sweater, red shoes, etc. He might be ready now for you to give him the secondary colors (green, orange and purple) to learn. You could also use a paintbook in which you ask him to color some part of the person or thing with one colored crayon, another part with another color, and so on.

Following the color activity numbers could now be introduced. He will, no doubt, have had some knowledge of these already, but may be not in a learning situation. You could begin by counting five fingers, five toes. However, concentrate only on him learning up to three at this time but expose him to all numbers up to, and including, five. He could count the number of hats the doll has, the number of shoes, the number of socks, etc. Instead of counting the dolls clothes, he could count his own. The counting of numbers could come naturally in many ways in his everyday experiences.

For the actual language part you could use the doll, and/or picture doll, to learn the parts of the head, as suggested at the beginning of the lesson. Then always transfer the learning experience to his own person; for example, when you talk about the doll's eyes, then show him, or ask him, where his eyes are, then indicate your own eyes. Henceforth, when the opportunity arises, make use of this knowledge in his everyday experiences. For the clothing, mentioned at the beginning of the lesson, make use of the doll, or the picture, or both, and transfer the names of each garment to his own clothing each time the information is needed in a natural situation in his daily life at home; for example, when you are dressing or undressing him, or when he is doing these things for himself, always name each article.

The lesson would be concluded with the musical activity of your choice. As listening is the basis for the whole lesson, the musical activity reinforces the listening habit — reinforces, that is, if the activity is interesting to the child. Since speech is rhythmical, the musical rhythmic patterns are a useful aid to develop the rhythmical patterns of speech.

You might require four lessons, maybe eight, maybe more, maybe less, to cover this lesson unit adequately. Some children will require less, some will require more. This is true of all children. Each develops at an individual rate. You should know the rate of your child's achievement and work accordingly. By this time you should know how much you and he can achieve well in a lesson period. The amount done will vary from day to day and from week to week. This is a normal development.

Lesson 13

The theme of this lesson series could be *foods.* Part one could be on the various vegetables, part two on the fruits, and part three on the various types of drinks. You might want to omit this unit theme if the child has already learned the names through other lessons or in everyday experiences. If he has not learned them, then this lesson series would be a necessary part of his learning experience. Again, he will not learn every name, and he is not likely, at this stage, to learn perfectly the names he can, or attempts, to say. Improvement comes through continued use of the word. If he continues to use each word every time he can use the names and actions in their appropriate place of use, he will improve his performances with the spoken word.

Begin the lesson with the discrimination of sounds using noisemakers of similar pitches. Use also two more vowel sounds such as "o" and "oo." Use the same procedures for the discrimination of sounds as you have been doing. All visual clues must be eliminated, and his responses must be to auditory clues alone. He should be achieving nearly 100 per cent accuracy in his responses now. This step is to set the tone for the whole lesson — good listening.

Various colored vegetables (plain paper could be colored by the child, or colored pictures) could be planted in a make-believe or picture garden or pasted in a scrapbook for color work. A color book with these pictures could also be used. You might ask him to color the carrot orange, the pea green, etc. You will always use the language words and the speech appropriate to the theme. Keep the speech you use for this part simple in content. The picture, or colored-paper picture, fruits could be hung on a tree made as an outline on plain white paper, or on brown wrapping paper. The various cold drinks (water, milk, orange juice, coca cola, (Coke), lemonade, etc.) could be placed in a paper refrigerator or a toy one.

For the number work you and your child could count the number of vegetables you had, or count the number of just one variety such as carrots. (You would, of course, have to have the number of these foods you wanted for this activity as part of the lesson.) Transfer the knowledge of counting over into everday living. When you give him an apple, or two cookies, or three jelly beans, you and he count them one by one each time until he learns to count them himself.

For the language activity have him put the picture vegetables (or fruits, or drinks) on the flannelboard, as you ask him to do this one at a time. (The flannelboard can be made by tacking a piece of plain flannel material to a piece of plywood the size you wanted.) You could have him store the vegetables in a toy refrigerator or paste each item on to a picture refrigerator. For a variation you could have him cut out from a magazine, one by one, these vegetables as you ask for them. This can be done if he is at the stage where he can cut out things. Then, have him paste these pictures in his scrapbook. It would be best to have him cut out one vegetable that you had asked for and then have him paste this one in the scrapbook, before asking for another. You might only get one or two cut out in one lesson. That is fine; proceed at the child's rate. The next day go over these items in the scrapbook and have him name each and tell you what is done with each, if he is ready for this stage of telling the use of each.

Learn a song about the above foods, if you can do this, or can find such a song. Or you can use the record player, or piano, and the music of your choice. Be sure that he is active, singing, clapping, or whatever, to the rhythmic pattern of the song of music.

Daily use must be made of the names of the above foods, so that he gets the necessary practice for spontaneous use in his speech. For example, at mealtimes refer to the vegetables he is eating, the fruit he is enjoying, the drink he is drinking.

The length of the lesson by now could likely be increased to forty minutes. The actual lesson should be done only once per day. There will be occasional days when you will have no time for a lesson. Do not worry about these times. He can be learning in the everyday activities. You must choose the best time of the day for the lessons. A suggested time is right after breakfast when he is still fresh and before he becomes involved in everyday play with the other members of the family or the neighborhood children.

Lesson 14

This series could be a unit on utensils. The first part could make use of the cutlery — knife, fork, spoon (various sizes); the second part could be on the various dishes — plate, bowl, cup, glass, etc.; and the third part on the kitchenware — pots, pans, lids, etc. The units do not have to follow in the order mentioned, nor do all parts have to be covered. You must decide what you will do. You may feel no need for the child to practice in any of these areas; he may already know the names of the various objects. You may want to proceed with transportation instead. Again you can make use of the toy materials, or you can construct the lesson material from whatever you have at hand. Make each as realistic as possible. The activities would be in the form of constructive play.

The lesson would begin with sound discrimination. Use the type of procedures and materials similar to the previous lesson. If the vowels — $\bar{a},\bar{e},\bar{i},\bar{o},\bar{u},a,ah,e,i,u,oo,ow,oy$ — have been practiced for discrimination, then combine two of these in random order and continue to practice for response to auditory stimulation only. Do not use more than two vowels at a time for each lesson.

For a color activity, which should be based on the particular theme for the lesson, you could have him cut out a spoon, or fork, or knife, which you had outlined, and have him color each; or you could have him cut out a picture of each of these colored objects from a magazine, as you ask for each one, and then have him paste each in his scrapbook. Again, cut and paste each before going on to a second one. Although it has not been stated each time, you will be naming each of the objects, talking about each in simple language, asking him questions about each and expecting verbal responses from him at all times. For example, you could tell him the knife is sharp; you could ask him what he does with a knife (or spoon). It does not matter if his speech is not perfect, as long as he is trying to do his best. Defects in his speech will be improved or corrected when he has formal speech lessons, or hearing therapy, or when he enters school. It is vastly more important that he is developing a word and sentence vocabulary now. A number activity can be easily made with the use of the objects suggested in the theme. He should be familiar with at least the numbers 1 to 5 by now. You may even have gone beyond this already, if the child was ready for it. Continue to add to the numbers: after 5 add 6, then 7, etc.

This might be a good time to introduce formal exposure to individual speech sounds. Begin with those consonants that are most easily seen such as (b), (p), (m). Have a large printed form of the sound to be used. Say (b) for him several times. Have him say it after you. Place the card or paper with the printed letter on the flannelboard, or have him paste it in his scrapbook, using a fresh page for each sound as you present one. Present only one consonant sound in a lesson and use that one for a review for the following lesson or lessons, until he is familiar with it before proceeding to the next consonant. Follow the production of the sound with words having the sound in the initial position such as ball, baby, boat, bat, Bobby, bean, bead, etc. These words could be represented with pictures which he could cut out and paste in his scrapbook under the letter (b). These words should also be reviewed in the following lessons. If he is not at the cutting out stage, you should do this and he can paste the picture in the scrapbook. The pictures could also be used for putting on the flannelboard instead of in the scrapbook and removing them one by one, as you make the request. You could have him put these on the wall with Sticky Tac,® or on a special board you use for this purpose. At this stage of learning, use the words with the sound only at the first of the word. In order of easy visibility, the consonants are p, b, m; f, v,; th, y; t, d, n, l.; s, sh; wh, w; r, z; k, g, h; ch, j,; q, x. However, in taking all of one group, one after the other, may cause confusion for the child, if he has to depend primarily on vision for learning. For example, p, b, m, all look alike on the lips. Used in isolation the child will not know which one you are saying unless he can hear. For the visual learner he will learn the difference when the sounds are used in words and he has learned the words. As long as the child can hear the difference in the sounds he and you will have no difficulty.

The language activity, based on the theme, could be prepared in whatever form you wish for variety. The consonant words used in the consonant-sound activity above could be taken from the theme of the lesson. For example, if the theme was *dishes,* words used could be bowl, butter dish, broiler for the above theme when the consonant used was (b). The language activity, consonant-sound and consonant-words drill could all form one part of the overall lesson. Or you might like to keep the two parts separate sometimes, combined at other times.

The lesson should, as usual, end with a brief musical activity. For this particular lesson you might produce a rhythm band with the knives, spoons, forks, and make your own music with a definite rhythm to which the child could keep time. You could have other members of the family participate in this activity.

Do not use too many words at a time with the individual sounds, if this part is to be different from the language activity. Three or four words should be enough. If used as a separate activity, the drill on the single sound and the words should not take more than five to ten minutes of the whole lesson.

By now the child should be able to do from forty-five to fifty or sixty minutes of work activity. Do not keep him longer than this, even though he may indicate his willingness to continue. Some days you may find the time that you can keep his attention is less than usual; if this happens, do not try to push him beyond what he is willing to do at that time; encourage him to do more but do not push him. As long as an interest is maintained he will be willing to work. If he does not work as long one day, then the next lesson may be extended to five to ten minutes over the hour, if the child is in the mood to work longer. But do not go beyond this time.

You may have problems keeping his interest when he knows the other children have gone outdoors to play. It might be wise to arrange the activities of the other children after breakfast so that he is not aware they have gone outside to play.

Continue to keep a progress book showing the new achievements as each is made. You will not necessarily have something new to report each day, or even each week, but, when there is something to report, remember to record it.

A continuing use of the scrapbook keeps readily available material for review.

Lesson 15

You could follow the themes listed at the back of this book as they are indicated or you could change the order to suit the needs and level of development at which your child is ready to function. Suppose that the topic is transportation. This could be divided into (a) those vehicles that travel on the road, e.g. truck, car, bus, station wagon, etc.; (b) those that travel on rails; (c) those that fly in the air, e.g. airplane, bomber, helicopter; and (d) those that work on the land, tractor, jeep, wagon, sleigh. Toy specimen or pictures could be used. Transference of the names to the actual object would be made following the lesson and every time henceforth that the child would see any of these objects in everyday experiences.

The lesson would begin with the discrimination of sound. The car horn and bicycle horn could be used for one lesson of this series. A recorded sound of each could be used in the place of the sound produced by the toy horn. The vowels that could be used for discrimination could be a combination of any two vowels already learned or a new one that might not yet have been used. For example, you could use (ah) and (u), or (a) and (ah). These could be appropriate for the theme of the lesson. (Wherever the vowels used could be tied in with the lesson theme, this should be done.)

All colors should be incorporated into the lessons by now. That is, you can be making use of any color that is appropriate for the theme. Do not use more than four colors in any one lesson. For example, you could have several small colored cars, of the colors you wanted to use, and have a race track outlined in squares on cardboard and a spinner with numbers. When he spins, the child could move his one colored car the number of squares corresponding to the number he had on the spinner. The next turn it could be another colored car he would move. This could be used as a combination color and number activity. You could just as easily use picture cars as toys ones.

For the activity of consonant recognition in isolation and in words, (p) and (t) could be used, or either one of them alone — whatever you feel the child can handle at this point without frustration. Following the production of the sound in isolation and pasting the printed form in his scrapbook, the words are presented. These are said and the pictures are shown for each word as it is said. (The pictures could be those you draw yourself.) Instead of putting the isolated sound and words in the scrapbook, each could be tacked to the wall or board, with Sticky Tac. The child must say the name of each object every time he or you handle it. The next lesson you could paste them in the book and use for a review of the sound and words. Do not use more than three or four words at a time. You must remember to have a review of the previous sound, or sounds, before you present the new sound. All the previous words do not need to be reviewed each time; but you should keep going back over as many as time will allow every week. Do not hesitate to repeat words, sounds, and sentences as often as they must be repeated in order that the child learn to recognize them and to remember them from auditory or visual stimulation.

The language activity may be combined with the presentation of the words in the activity above, or it may be used as a separate activity. For example, the child and you might be going to grandmother's on the airplane. The whole lesson could be based on what would happen and what you would do in preparing for such a trip. The preparation for the trip, the drive to the airport, boarding the plane, what it was like on the airplane, and the arrival at the airport in the city to which you are going. Actually you would have enough material in this for several lessons. The consonant sound that you choose might be using (p). You would have such words as plane, put, pants (for wearing and packing), packing, party, etc. Even if you did not take the trip in actuality, it still could be an imaginary trip. You could have a picture of grandmother, her house, her car, her pony; you could have a suitcase, clothes to be packed, closing the house, the car, the drive to the airport, picture of an airport, plane, and so on.

The musical step would be tied in as closely as possible to the theme of the lesson. If this is not possible choose some form of musical activity, where the child must respond actively.

The lesson now should be fifty to sixty minutes long. You should choose the best time of day that is suitable for you and when the child is freshest. This provides the best climate for the child to learn.

SUMMARY

A series of lesson plans have been outlined. These begin with the development of the awareness of sound and proceeds to gross discrimination of sound then to a finer discrimination of sounds. Vocabulary building is a continuous process. When this part has developed some of the finer discrimination of speech sounds is introduced. Colors and numbers form part of the process of vocabulary building and development of language concepts. Musical activities are used to impart to the child the sense of the rhythm patterns which are an important aspect of our speech. The lessons are graded to progress from the easy to the more difficult. Suggestions for variations are given in order to allow for flexibility in the lessons. The series is intended to give materials and procedures that cover a period of one and one-half to two years.

READING MATERIALS

BOOKS

Lowell, Edgar L., and Stoner, Marguerite: Play It By Ear: (Auditory Training Games) John Tracy Clinic. Los Angeles, Wolfer Publishing Company, 1960.
Myklebust, Helmer R.: Your Dear Child. Springfield, Thomas, 1950.
                    If You Have A Deaf Child — A Collection of Helpful Hints to Mothers of Preschool Deaf Children. Urbana (Ill.), U. of Illinois, 1953.
Ronnei, Eleanor C., and Porter, Joan: Tim And His Hearing Aid. Alexander Graham Bell Association for the Deaf Inc. The Volta Bureau, 1537 35th Street, N.W., Washington, D.C. 20007, 1951.

PERIODICALS

American Annals of the Deaf, Editorial Office, Gallaudet College, Washington, D.C. 20002.
Hearing and Speech News, National Association of Hearing and Speech Agencies, 919 18th Street, N.W., Washington, D.C. 20002.
Volta Review, The Alexander Graham Bell Association for the Deaf Inc., 1537 35th Street, N.W., Washington, D.C. 20007.

CATALOGS FOR SOURCE MATERIALS

You can write for these catalogs.
American Guidance Service, Inc., Publishers' Building, Circle Pines, Minnesota 55014.
Beckley-Cardy, 1900 North Narraganseth Avenue, Chicago, Illinois 60639.
Catalog of Early Childhood Materials, Webster Division, McGraw-Hill Company, Manchester Road, Manchester, Missouri 63011.
Community Playthings, Rifton, New York 12471.
Constructive Playthings, 1040 East 85th Street, Kansas City, Missouri 64131.
Creative Playthings, Inc., Princeton, New Jersey 08540.
Speech and Language Materials, Inc., P.O. Box 721, Tulsa, Oklahoma 74101.
    There are many stores where materials can be purchased; for example, Woolworth's, Kresge's, toy shops, the toy departments of department stores and drug stores.

CATALOGS FOR RECORDS

Children's Music Center, Inc., 5373 West Pico Boulevard, Los Angeles,
   California 90019.
Educational Record Sales, 157 Chambers Street, New York City, New York
   10007 (Songs for Children With Special Needs — $4.95 — recommended).
Lyons Band Instrument Company, 223 West Lake Street, Chicago, Illinois.
Stanley Bowmar Company, Inc., 4 Broadway, Valhalla, New York 10595.

   There are many good children's records that can be obtained through the
children's record section at your local record store. Each record usually
contains a description of the contents and suggested age. One record which is
an auditory training album and manual is WHAT'S ITS NAME? by the Maico
Hearing Aid Company, Minneapolis, Minnesota, at a cost of $10.75.

Appendix B

The following list of materials might help make your job of teaching your child speech and language somewhat easier.

BOOKS

6 Months to 1 Year

Animal — A Hampton cloth book $1.50

Baby Animals

Baby's Book of Animals —Cloth picture book by Lowe. James and Jonathan, Inc.

Baby's Mother Goose — Illustrated by Alice Schlesinger-McLoughlin Bros. Publisher 1.95

Farm Animals — Illustrated by Imma Wilde 1.50

Favorite Nursery Songs — Phyllis Brown O'Lanian-Random House 1.00

Mother Goose by Wonder Books, A division of Grosset and Dunlap, Inc. .59

Play With Me — Esther and Eloise Wilkins–Golden Book, Golden Press, New York .29

1 Year to 2 Years

A Child's Good Night Book — Margaret Wise Brown

Goodnight Moon — Margaret Wise Brown, Harper and Row 2.50

Johnny Crow's Garden — Leslie Brooks 2.50

The Duck — Photographs by Ylla and text by Margaret Wise Brown

Sturdi-Contour Books — by Wonder Books, Division of Grosset and Dunlap

2 Years to 3 Years

All By Himself — by Kay Clark, A Plakie Product Creative Playthings, Princeton, New Jersey

Big and Little — A Big Golden Book, Golden Press 1.00

Golden Clock Books — Golden Press 1.00

Golden Happy Puppy Book — Golden Press 1.00

Golden Shape Books — Golden Press, New York .29

73

3 Years to 4 Years

All Fall Down — Gene Zion, Harper and Row 2.95

Dr. Seuss Books

Golden Counting Books — A Golden Play and Learn Book by Roberta Miller, Golden Press 1.00

Kittens — Sharon Banigan, James and Johnathan, Inc. .39

Millions of Cats — Wanda Gay, Coward-McCann 2.50

Puppies — Sharon Banigan, James and Johnathan, Inc. .39

Children 4 years to 5 years still enjoy nursery rhymes. They enjoy reciting them and telling stories. Animal stories are very popular. It is suggested that you take your four or five-year-old to the library. Most libraries have children's rooms. Help your child select one or two books. The library will be a strange place to him at first, so do not hurry him. Get acquainted with your librarian because she can help your child select suitable books. For additional assistance in choosing reading matter for your child, you might want to consult *A Parent's Guide to Children's Reading for Parents and Teachers of Children Under 13.* This book is by Nancy Larrick and is sponsored by the National Book Committee, Inc. It can be purchased for $.50. It lists many good books with a short description of the content and gives the recommended age.

OUTLINE FOR A PROGRAM IN AUDITORY TRAINING FOR THE PRESCHOOL CHILD

Each hour lesson is to consist of the following:

1. developing the awareness of sound
   then
   discrimination of gross sounds
   then
   discrimination of finer sounds
   a. percussion toys, e.g., drum, bell, horn, clacker, etc.
   b. recorded materials
   c. speech sounds — vowels
2. one color activity
   (a) primary colors — blue, red, yellow
   (b) secondary colors — green, orange, purple
   (c) black, white, pink, brown, gray
3. one number activity — when the child is ready for it 1 to 3 to 5 to 6 to 7 to 8 to 9 to 10
4. isolated speech sounds
   (a) first one consonant
   (b) then two consonants
   (c) words for each consonant — pictures are used with the words.
5. language activity, one or two activities
   Use toy objects, pictures and real objects eventually.
6. music, one activity
   Have the child always participate actively.

When you are just beginning the lessons you will not use all six activities. Follow the individual lessons outlined in the book. When you have reached Part II you will have reached the outlined lesson noted above.

The two words that you will use most often are *Watch* and *Listen*. These words can at first be reinforced by pointing to the eyes and to the ears.

Do not use any one group of material for more than one activity; that is, what you have used for colors should not be used again for numbers. Fresh material keeps the interest high, and this is necessary if you are to get the cooperation of the very young child.

THEMES OF WEEKLY OR MONTHLY LESSONS

1. Family: (a) introduction of family and life at home (b) family on a picnic (c) family at the zoo.
   Note: With the very young child, this must be modified to his level of learning.
2. The Person: (a) parts of the body (b) indoor clothing (c) outdoor clothing.
3. Foods: (a) vegetables (b) fruits (c) drinks.
4. Utensils: (a) cutlery (b) dishes (c) kitchenware.
5. Furniture: (a) living room (b) bedroom (c) bathroom (d) kitchen.
6. Transportation: (a) cars (b) buses (c) airplanes (d) trucks (e) tractors (f) trains.
7. Animals: (a) domestic (b) wild (c) zoo.
8. Shopping: (a) grocery (b) drug store (c) clothing.
9. Weather: (a) sunny (b) rainy (c) snowy.
10. Clothing: (a) for indoors (b) for outdoors (c) for sleeping (d) for swimming.
11. Seasons: (a) spring (b) summer (c) autumn (d) winter.
    The type of clothing worn during each season could be taken at this time, too.
12. Games: (a) played in the spring (b) played in the summer (c) played in the autumn (d) played in the winter.
13. Sports: (a) baseball (b) football (c) hockey (d) soccer.
14. Community Helpers: (a) policeman (b) fireman (c) mailman (d) milkman (e) farmer.
15. The Farm: (a) house and surroundings (b) barn, surroundings and occupants (c) meadows (d) pastures.
16. Children's Games: (a) hide-and-seek (b) hop-scotch (c) lotto.
17. Plant Life: (a) outdoor flowers (b) indoor plants and flowers (c) shrubs and trees.
18. Nursery Rhymes: (a) Ten Little Indians (b) Humpty-Dumpty (c) Mary Had a Little Lamb, etc.
19. Others: (a) fish (b) birds (c) reptiles.

Only one of each theme, e.g. part (a), must be used for any one lesson. You may have to repeat the theme of (a) several times with different material each time such as toy objects one time, flannel board objects another, and picture objects another time. The lesson themes will need to be adapted to the age and learning language level for the individual child.

You should plan your lesson in advance and know what materials you will need and have these ready before the lesson.

You must continue to encourage the child to imitate speech sounds and babbling until he has reached the stage of imitating words. After this stage he must be encouraged to use words in combination such as red car, yellow airplane, and so on into simple sentences.

For the young child just beginning, only #'s 1 and 2 of the lesson outline will be used at first. This will be increased to include #5 and #6. Modify the lesson to meet the age and language level of the child.

You must speak normally and in simple sentences for the young child. Do not talk so much that the child has not an opportunity to speak. The child should be encouraged to watch the lips, as well as listen. Always position yourself where your child can see your face clearly and easily. Be sure to get down to his level and do not have him looking up at you.

SUGGESTIONS FOR SOME WORDS
THAT COULD BE TAUGHT WITH UNITS

Family
mother, mommie
father, daddy
sister) names of
brother) each

Relatives
grandmother
grandfather
uncle) names of
aunt) each
cousin

Foods
fruits: apple, orange, etc.
vegetables: peas, bean, etc.
meats
desserts
staples: bread, sugar, butter, etc.

Drinks
water
milk
coke
soda

tea
coffee
chocolate

Utensils
glass
cup
saucer
mug
plate
dish
bowl
fork
spoon
knife
pan
pot
frying pan
teakettle
lid
tablecloth
placemat

Furniture
kitchen: chair, table, etc.

living room
dining room
bedroom
bathroom

Outside Home
front lawn
backyard
grass
tree
flowers
fence
gate
sidewalk
steps
clothesline
pole
bushes
garden
garbage cans

Parts of the Body
hair
face
nose
mouth
teeth
tongue
eyes
eyelashes
eyebrows
ears
arms
hands
fingers
thumb
body
legs
feet
toes
fingernails

toenails
heel
elbow
wrist
knee
skin
shoulder
lap

Clothing
dress
shirt
skirt
sweater
blouse
pants
socks
stockings
slip
shoes
boots
sandals
rubbers
coat
jacket
hat
cap
mittens
gloves
scarf
slippers
night clothes

Parts of Dress (Sweater, Blouse)
sleeves
cuff
buttons
fasteners
collar
belt

Toys
  doll
  truck
  car
  block
  building materials
  beads
  airplane
  games

Weather
  sun, sunny
  clouds, cloudy
  rain, rainy
  snow, snowy
  cold
  hot

Seasons
  Spring
  Summer
  Autumn
  Winter

Transportation
  car
  truck
  bus
  airplane: passenger
  train: freight
  bicycle
  tricycle
  motorcycle
  boat: row, yacht, motor, ocean-
     liner, launch

Farm Animals
  dog: bow-wow, woof, arf
  cat: meow
  cow: moo
  horse

  calf
  colt
  donkey
  goat
  sheep
  lamb: baa-baa
  rabbit

Farm Fowl
  duck: quack
  hen: caw-caw
  chick (chicken): peep-peep
  rooster: cock-a-doodle-do
  turkey: gobble
  goose: th-th-th

Zoo Animals
  camel
  bear
  giraffe
  elephant
  lion
  tiger
  leopard
  monkey
  gorilla
  deer
  antelope

Birds
  robin
  crow
  blackbird
  budgie
  canary
  parrot
  chickadee
  blue jay
  bluebird
  cardinal

Sea Animals
  seal
  walrus
  sea lion
  fish

Shopping
  drug store
  clothing store
  grocery store
  dime store
  furniture store
  hardware store
  department store
  lumber yard

Visit to
  restaurant
  dentist
  doctor
  movie
  theatre
  park
  church
  laundromat

Sports
  baseball
  football
  hockey
  soccer
  basketball
  golf
  badminton
  tennis
  horseback riding
  swimming
  skiing: snow, water
  skating

Community Helpers
  policeman

  fireman
  milkman
  postman, mailman
  newsboy
  truck driver
  pilot
  builder

Nursery Rhymes
  Mary Had a Little Lamb
  Little Boy Blue
  Little Miss Muffit
  Hickory Dickory Dock
  Baa, Baa, Black Sheep

Colors
  blue   )
  yellow) primary
  red   )
  orange)
  purple) secondary
  green)
  white
  black
  brown
  pink

Numbers
  1
  to
      5
  to
      10
  to
      15
  to
      20
  to
      25
  to
      100

INDEX